Lifesaving

Handbook of The Royal Life Saving Society United Kingdom

RLSS UK, River House, High Street, Broom, Warwickshire, B50 4HN
Telephone: 01789 773994   Fax : 01789 773995

Sixth Edition © 1995
The Royal Life Saving Society United Kingdom

Written & Edited by David Eaton MA, FIST, FIST (LS)
RLSS UK Tutor & Lifesaving Development Co-ordinator

ISBN : 0 907082 59 9

Graphic Design by Lisa Ellis
New Photography by Tim Fisher
Illustrations by Nicola Clements

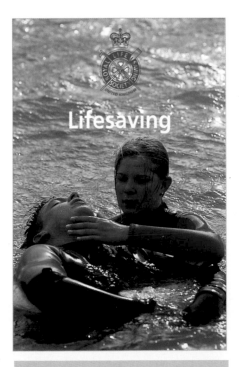

LIFESAVING

The Handbook

The Society's first handbook, used throughout the Commonwealth, was published in 1891. It was revised and reprinted on over 40 occasions until, in 1963, Branches in the United Kingdom, Canada, Australia and New Zealand published their own handbooks.

RLSS UK Handbook
1st Edition 1963
2nd Edition 1969
3rd Edition 1973

Consisting of four volumes:-
- Lifesaving & Water Safety
- Emergency Resuscitation
- Examiners' Manual
- On Guard (The Lifeguard Manual)

4th Edition 1978

Eight individual volumes contained within a separate ring binder:-
- Lifesaving and Water Safety
- Water Rescue Skills
- Teaching Water Safety
- Lifesaving Teacher's Guide
- Resuscitation and First Aid
- The Awards Scheme
- Lifeguard Manual
- Examiners Guide to the Award Scheme

5th Edition 1990

The first full colour lifesaving volume including chapters on water safety, swimming, survival, rescue principles and rescue skills.

6th Edition 1995 (reprinted with minor amendments 1997)
- Lifesaving

Other RLSS UK Publications
- Life Support
- Beach Lifeguarding
- Pool Lifeguard
- Specially Safe
- Swim, Survive, Save
- Rookie Trainer's Guide

Preface to the Sixth Edition of Lifesaving

Lifesaving in its broadest sense implies the saving of life through the prevention of accidents, personal survival and the rescue of others. Supervised aquatic activities in swimming pools, leisure centres and open water locations are immensely popular, but accidents often occur in places such as rivers, lakes, and canals where the presence of qualified lifeguards is rare. Even at the coast, many beaches are not patrolled. Sudden changes in climate and environment put people at risk throughout the year. For these reasons, all members of the community should learn the basic principles of lifesaving.

This book provides details of the skills and knowledge required to become a competent lifesaver. It contains chapters on water safety & accident prevention, swimming & diving, survival & self-rescue, rescue principles & skills, aftercare & support.

Since the fifth edition of 'Lifesaving' was published in 1990, the Royal Life Saving Society United Kingdom has played an increasingly prominent role in the promotion of water safety, swimming, survival, rescue, life support and first aid.

RLSS UK has campaigned successfully for the inclusion of swimming & water safety in the National Curriculum, provided a comprehensive training programme and awards structure for pool and beach lifeguards, promoted the importance of rescue training for swimming teachers and outdoor centre staff, participated successfully in national water safety and life support events, launched a number of exciting initiatives and developed strong links with lifesaving organisations worldwide.

We hope you find this book interesting, that you will refer to it regularly and use it to promote lifesaving throughout your local community.

Acknowledgements

The Editor wishes to acknowledge the considerable help given to the production of this publication by the Society's National Officers, Members of the National Education & Technical Committee, South Worcestershire Lifeguards, Coventry Sports Centre & the Staff at River House.

Technical Advisers	Peter Banham	Olive Bowes	Cavell Burchell
	Dr Anthony Handley	Declan Harte	Mary Hopkins
	Sheila Norman	Audrey O'Brien	Graham Pollard
	Brian Sims	Peter Whittall	Janet Wilson

Swimmers, Lifesavers and Lifeguards	Peter Banham	Sam Cross	Anthony Day
	Lisa Donavan	Sarah Evans	Vic Evans
	Adele Grasby	Mick Griffiths	Mark Gozdecki
	Richard Gozdecki	Mary Hopkins	Andrew Hoxley
	Paul Hoxley	Ian Lavender	Ruth Lawrence
	Alex Mellor	Liz McVeigh	Vicky Moseley
	Christine O'Brien	Sunita Patel	Vanisha Patel
	Nathan Pearce	Helen Phillips	Sandra Smith
	Luke Talbot	Julie Wilkinson	

1

Introduction to The Royal Life Saving Society UK

This chapter provides a brief picture of The Royal Life Saving Society UK (RLSS UK). On the following pages you will find information about:-

- history and development of lifesaving
- aims and structure of RLSS UK
- organisation of lifesaving in the UK
- promotion of lifesaving in the UK

History and Development of Lifesaving

The Royal Life Saving Society was formed in 1891 in an attempt to reduce the annual toll of 2,000 lives lost in drowning accidents in the United Kingdom - by publicising the causes of these accidents, by encouraging everyone to learn to swim and by teaching competent swimmers the methods by which a drowning person might be saved. In 1924, the Society was granted a Royal Charter by King George V; a supplemental Charter was granted by Queen Elizabeth in 1959.

Today The Royal Life Saving Society is the largest single organisation dedicated to the teaching of lifesaving and the prevention of drowning in the United Kingdom. It is active in over forty countries worldwide. The Society's Commonwealth Conference is held in the United Kingdom every five years and is attended by representatives from around the world. Special events and development workshops are held regularly on every continent organised by the Society's volunteer and professional officers.

RLSS Commonwealth has major Branches in Australia, Canada, New Zealand and the United Kingdom. In addition, lifesaving activities are particularly strong in the Far East, India and Africa. Member Branches and Honorary Representatives keep in touch with developments worldwide through the RLSS Commonwealth office in Stratford-upon-Avon, Warwickshire.

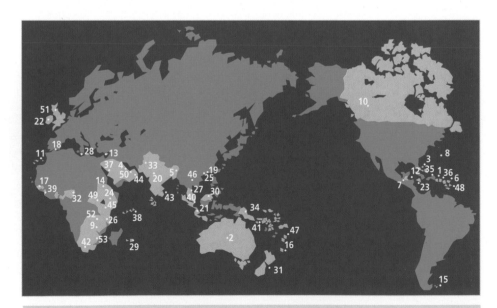

LOCATION OF RLSS ACTIVITY WORLDWIDE

Aims of The Royal Life Saving Society UK

The Royal Life Saving Society UK is committed to preventing loss of life from drowning and asphyxiation. To enable these aims to be achieved, the Society's members spend considerable time:-

- promoting water safety education and life support in the community
- training lifesavers and lifeguards in the areas of accident prevention, survival, rescue, life support, emergency aftercare and first aid
- researching the causes and effects of drowning and asphyxiation
- developing educational resources and technical expertise

Structure of The Royal Life Saving Society UK

RLSS UK has a network of administrative, consultative and decision-making bodies responsible for policy, research and development.

Headquarters

The Society's head office is in the village of Broom, twenty miles south of Birmingham, where a committed staff, led by an executive Director General, are responsible for managing the Society's affairs on a daily basis and meeting the needs of members across the country and overseas.

Management

The Director General and Executive Officers of RLSS UK based at River House report to the Society's Annual Branch Conference and to a number of elected volunteer committees, throughout the year.

These committees recommend policy and oversee the development of the Society's work in the UK. All committees and officers report to the National Management Board which is responsible for managing the Society's affairs and deciding policy in accordance with the wishes of the Annual Branch Conference.

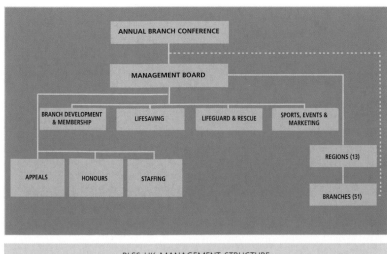

RLSS UK MANAGEMENT STRUCTURE

1

1

Branches

RLSS UK has 51 Branches throughout the United Kingdom and Ireland as well as a number of overseas and British Forces Branches. Each Branch has an Executive Committee responsible for the development of the Society's work at local level.

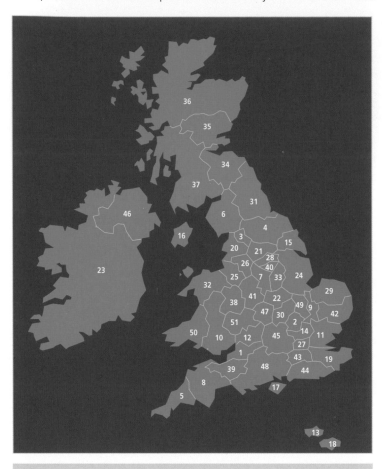

RLSS UK BRANCHES

Lifesaving Clubs

2,000 clubs and training centres promote lifesaving, whilst 150 volunteer lifeguard clubs patrol open water locations in and around the UK. These clubs and training centres focus on lifesaving skills, competitions and social events.

SAVING LIFE

Lifesaving

Promotion of Lifesaving in the UK

The Royal Life Saving Society UK pursues its aims through the following means:

Technical Services

RLSS UK provides leadership and specialist advice to voluntary and professional bodies on all aspects of lifesaving, lifeguarding, life support and aquatic accident prevention.

Public Awareness Campaigns

RLSS UK promotes important public water safety, lifesaving and life support messages through publicity campaigns, press releases, competitions and other events.

Education Programmes

RLSS UK provides training and award programmes in the areas of water safety, swimming, survival, lifesaving, lifeguarding, life support and aquatic first aid. In addition, the Society runs a modular programme for prospective trainers and assessors which contains a variety of core and specialist units linked to National Vocational Qualifications (NVQ).

Resources

A variety of educational resources from handbooks to resuscitation manikins and videos are available from RLSS UK Enterprises Ltd and Branch Awards and Sales Officers. All items are displayed in the Society's annual catalogue.

Research

In recent years, RLSS UK has been at the forefront of research into drownings, rescues and other matters of importance to lifesavers. This has depended on developing close relationships with other institutions and organisations. Findings from some of the research can be found later in this book.

Membership

RLSS UK offers membership to anyone interested in the Society's activities. Members are entitled to a membership card, personal accident and public liability insurance as well as to receive the Society's magazine 'Lifeguard'.

BOOKS, AWARDS AND RESOURCES

Competitions

RLSS UK holds regular lifesaving and lifeguard competitions in its Branches and Regions. National Championships are held annually at suitable indoor and outdoor venues. In addition, RLSS UK has sent teams in recent years to compete in European, Commonwealth and World lifesaving and lifeguarding competitions.

Special Conferences and Events

RLSS UK has hosted a number of major conferences and seminars over the past few years, which have been attended by leading national and international experts in the fields of lifesaving, lifeguarding and life support.

1

RLSS COMMONWEALTH

INTERNATIONAL
LIFE SAVING FEDERATION

Liaison with Other Organisations

The Society has a close working relationship with a large number of organisations. These include:

- Department for Education (DFE)
- Sports Council
- Amateur Swimming Association (ASA)
- Swimming Teachers' Association (STA)
- Royal Society for the Prevention of Accidents (RoSPA)
- Surf Life Saving Association of Great Britain (SLSA-GB)
- Institute of Sport & Recreation Management (ISRM)
- Institute of Leisure and Amenity Management (ILAM)
- Resuscitation Council - United Kingdom
- Royal National Lifeboat Institution (RNLI)

In addition, RLSS UK maintains close links with all Commonwealth Branches and members worldwide from its Headquarters at River House and through the Commonwealth Secretariat from its offices in Stratford-upon-Avon.

RLSS UK is a participating and founder member of the International Life Saving Federation (ILS) which unites lifesavers and lifeguards from around the world in the discussion of technical matters as well as in competition.

Checking your Understanding of The Royal Life Saving Society UK

The following questions are designed to check your knowledge and understanding of the Royal Life Saving Society United Kingdom, as described in this chapter; alongside each question is the relevant page reference.

page 6   When was The Royal Life Saving Society founded?
page 7   What are the aims of The Royal Life Saving Society UK?
page 8   How many RLSS UK Branches are there?
page 9   In what ways does RLSS UK develop and pursue its aims?
page 10   With what other organisations does RLSS UK work?

RESCUE TRAINING

Summary

The Royal Life Saving Society UK is the major lifesaving organisation in the country. It needs your support to develop and promote lifesaving and lifeguarding in the community. Why not join now or become a member of your local lifeguard or lifesaving club. If you are already a member, you could become involved in your local Branch Executive or seek election to one of the Society's national committees. Whatever you decide to do or whatever time you have got to give, remember that lifesaving education saves lives.

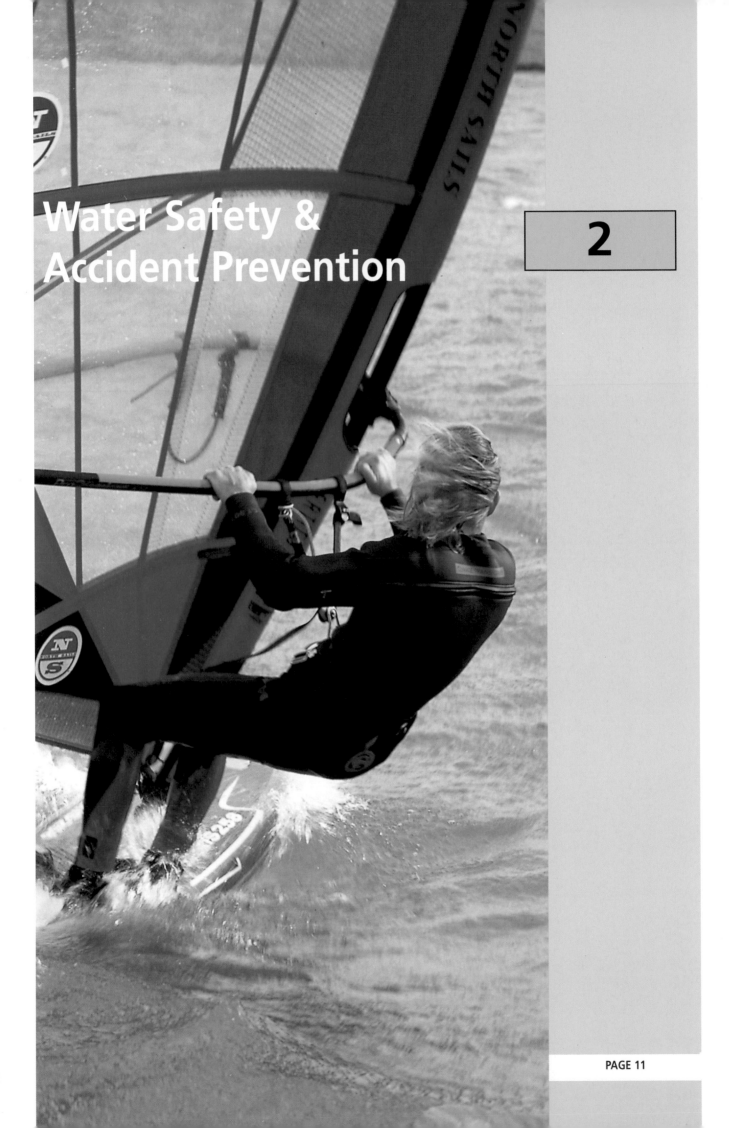

Water Safety & Accident Prevention

2

Introduction to Water Safety & Accident Prevention

This chapter provides information on the causes of drownings and on effective water safety education. It also offers guidance on preventing accidents in a number of different aquatic environments. On the following pages you will find information on:

2

- drowning chain
- research into drownings
- safety guidelines for aquatic activities
- safety equipment & emergency action
- training and assessing accident prevention

DROWNING CHAIN

Drowning Chain

Drownings and accidents in and around water follow a general pattern which can best be described as a chain of linked events. Each of the links can lead to direct injury or to the next link.

The concept of the chain suggests that where one or more of these links is evident, an aquatic accident is likely; where all five links occur a serious aquatic accident will result. Each link of the chain can be more fully described as:-

- ignorance, disregard or misjudgement of your own ability
- uninformed or unprotected access to a hazard
- incompetent or absence of supervision, especially of the young and the elderly
- inability to cope when an emergency situation arises

Breaking the Drowning Chain

A knowledge of water safety should reduce the likelihood of a drowning occurring. Therefore it makes sense to attempt to break the drowning chain by:-

- educating people on how to recognise and avoid dangerous situations
- denying and restricting open access to water hazards
- providing information leaflets and signs
- ensuring that those who supervise are suitably trained and competent
- acquiring competent swimming, personal survival and rescue skills
- making rescuers and rescue equipment readily available

Research into Drownings

Over the past twenty years or so, the Royal Life Saving Society has been at the forefront of research into drownings and has initiated a number of important research projects.

In the latter part of the nineteenth century, an estimated 2000 people drowned in the sea and inland water areas around Britain each year. Since then, the numbers have steadily reduced.

2

Today, 500 people, on average, drown each year in British waters. HM Coastguard respond to over 8,000 incidents and the Royal National Lifeboat Institution (RNLI) rescues over 1,500 persons annually (HM Coastguard & RNLI statistics).

Such statistics justified a major analysis of where, why, when and how people get into difficulty. Between 1981 and 1983, RLSS UK produced two important reports on drownings in the British Isles in collaboration with the Association of Chief Police Officers. These reports established the standards for future drownings research.

At the end of the 1980s, the Royal Society for the Prevention of Accidents (RoSPA) started to produce annual drowning statistics based on information received from national and local media. These figures highlighted seasonal and regional differences and also suggested a gradual decline in the number of drownings occurring in UK waters each year.

Since 1992, RLSS UK has undertaken a major research project into the causes of drownings in and around the United Kingdom, again in conjunction with the Association of Police Officers. The key elements of the findings so far are outlined below.

Location of Drownings

A wide variety of water environments are associated with drownings. Open water areas predominate; however it should be noted that over 10% of reported incidents occur annually in and around the home.

Drownings are more likely to occur in unprotected or unsupervised water areas. While lifeguard patrols have helped to reduce the number of deaths by drowning in swimming pools and open water, RLSS UK continues to highlight the dangers of all water environments.

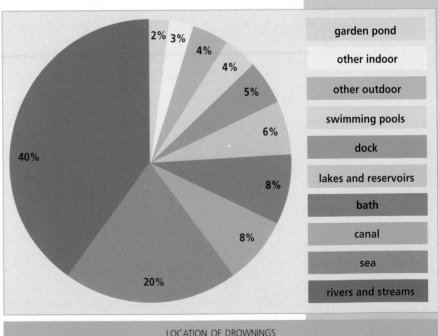

LOCATION OF DROWNINGS

2

Age & Sex of Casualties

In all age groups, male drownings dominate the statistics. There is a noticeable peak among active males of 15-34 age group.

Time of Year

The popular view that drownings increases during the summer months is confirmed by these statistics. Yet over 60 drownings took place in 1994 during the winter months of December and January.

Activity before Drowning

Drowning casualties may be involved in a wide variety of activities. Many casualties are often only a few metres from safety. Many boating accidents are the result of a lack of knowledge and skill in the management of boats. Furthermore, casualties have usually failed to take adequate safety precautions.

Alcohol and Drownings

Alcohol is the most popular drug in western society and is a contributing factor in many drowning cases every year. Only one alcoholic drink is needed to seriously impair judgement and reflexes and make most water activities unsafe. Anyone who has been drinking should be discouraged from entering the water. Remember, alcohol affects balance, judgement and slows down movement.

The Royal Life Saving Society is committed to reducing the number of lives lost annually through drowning. It is because of these statistics that the main focus of the Society's work is centred on:

- educating the whole community about the dangers of water
- training volunteers to become competent lifesavers
- ensuring that aquatic facilities are adequately supervised by trained lifeguards

Water Safety Education

The Society promotes water safety through its comprehensive education programme. At present, the mainstays of this programme are the RLSS UK National Curriculum Water Safety Pack and Video and the dynamic Rookie Lifeguard Training Scheme. Both these packages are aimed at the junior end of the market, as research has shown that effective water safety education starts with children.

In addition, the Society promotes knowledge and understanding of water safety principles through all its major swimming, lifesaving and lifeguarding awards.

WATER SAFETY AND ROOKIE LIFEGUARD PUBLICITY MATERIALS

Lifesaving

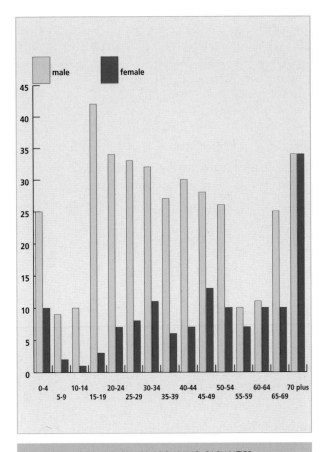

AGE AND SEX OF DROWNING CASUALTIES

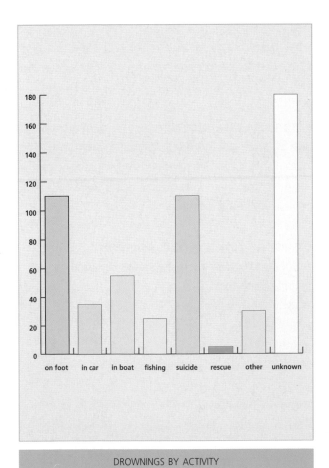

DROWNINGS BY ACTIVITY

DROWNINGS BY TIME OF YEAR

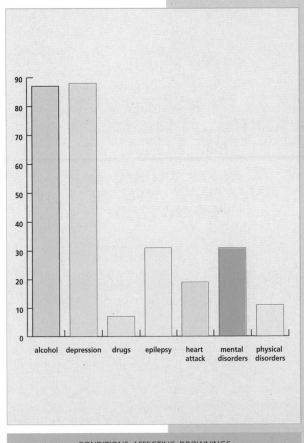

CONDITIONS AFFECTING DROWNINGS

WATER SAFETY CODE

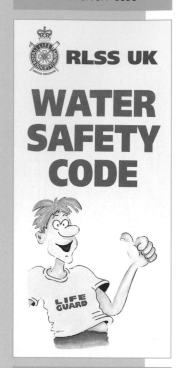

WATER SAFETY CODE LEAFLET

WATER SAFETY SIGN

Water Safety Code

RLSS UK and RoSPA have developed a joint water safety code, which is endorsed by other swimming and water safety organisations. It appears in all the Society's water safety publications and resource materials.

Water Safety Guidelines

Many people are attracted to activities in, on and around water. For children, in particular, water is fascinating. Unfortunately, a large percentage of deaths by drowning, occur in seemingly harmless locations (from domestic baths to paddling pools). It is, therefore, important that everyone, from adults to children, has a clear understanding of water safety. Water safety involves:

- knowing that each water location whether sea, river or lake has its own particular hazards
- knowing how to behave when in, on or near water, thus helping to prevent accidents
- being able to swim well in a variety of conditions and environments
- being confident but careful in and around water
- learning how to look after yourself and survive in extreme and often unexpected conditions
- being able to help other people who are in difficulty in the water
- being aware of potential water hazards in and around the home

Health and Safety in Water

In recent years, water pollution has been recognised as a major problem worldwide. Many beaches along the coastline have become permanently damaged by oil, sewage and litter pollution. The same problems have affected inland rivers, steams, and lakes.

While measures are being taken to alleviate the damage to the environment, many locations are now unsuitable for swimming. The National Rivers Authority, your local Water Board and your local council environmental health officers are responsible for monitoring and maintaining water quality across the country.

- check for notices indicating safety of beach and water
- look carefully at the condition of the water and its surroundings
- avoid drinking untreated water
- keep children away from dirty beaches
- avoid entering stagnant or slow moving water
- wash or shower after swimming
- cover minor scratches on exposed parts of the body with waterproof plasters
- use footwear to avoid cutting feet

POLLUTED WATER

Safety at Home

Many drowning accidents happen in and around the home; often this is because familiar surroundings are expected to be safe. Washing machines, paddling pools, water butts, basins and baths are all potential hazards to a small child. Keep children under constant supervision, especially when in or near water. Always remember to:

BABY IN BATH

- fence in private swimming pools and include self-closing gates
- keep garden gates closed and locked and water butts covered
- keep fish ponds covered with chicken wire which is secured at the edge
- install a swimming pool cover that can be firmly secured
- empty paddling pools, baths and buckets after use
- keep bath plugs out of the reach of small children
- supervise children's bath time
- keep young children away from washing machines

SAFETY IN THE KITCHEN

Drownings have occured in as little as six inches of water. While the most vigilant parent or child minder may not be able to prevent an unexpected accident occurring, it is possible to reduce the dangers by taking the precautions listed above. Safety begins at home.

FUN IN THE SWIMMING POOL

Lifesaving

Safety in Swimming Pools

Swimming continues to be one of the most popular recreational activities. Facilities for water recreation are plentiful, yet emergencies occur because people of all ages often over estimate their capabilities. The best guidance on swimming pool safety is to be found in the Sports Council publication, 'Safety in Swimming Pools', which formed the basis of the Health and Safety Executive investigation into public swimming facilities and in the RLSS UK publication, 'Pool Lifeguarding', which is used throughout the leisure industry. Always follow these simple rules:

- listen to the lifeguards
- leave the pool when instructed by a lifeguard
- read and obey notices giving advice to swimmers
- check the depth markings on the poolside to see where it is best to swim and dive
- walk when on the poolside
- stay away from deep water unless you are a competent swimmer
- follow the pool management's instructions regarding flumes and wave machines
- make sure the water is clear before diving and jumping in

Emergency Pool Procedures

Swimmers and lifesavers should be aware of the following procedures used by all public pools for dealing with emergencies:

FUN SESSIONS AT THE POOL

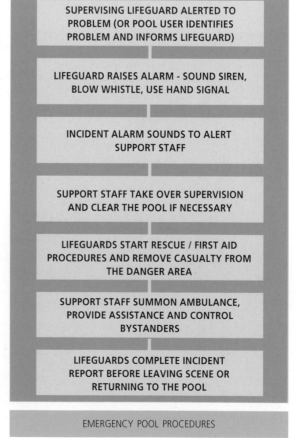

SUPERVISING LIFEGUARD ALERTED TO PROBLEM (OR POOL USER IDENTIFIES PROBLEM AND INFORMS LIFEGUARD)

LIFEGUARD RAISES ALARM - SOUND SIREN, BLOW WHISTLE, USE HAND SIGNAL

INCIDENT ALARM SOUNDS TO ALERT SUPPORT STAFF

SUPPORT STAFF TAKE OVER SUPERVISION AND CLEAR THE POOL IF NECESSARY

LIFEGUARDS START RESCUE / FIRST AID PROCEDURES AND REMOVE CASUALTY FROM THE DANGER AREA

SUPPORT STAFF SUMMON AMBULANCE, PROVIDE ASSISTANCE AND CONTROL BYSTANDERS

LIFEGUARDS COMPLETE INCIDENT REPORT BEFORE LEAVING SCENE OR RETURNING TO THE POOL

EMERGENCY POOL PROCEDURES

Lifesaving

Safety by Open Water

More and more people are spending their leisure time in, on and around water. Over recent years, this has brought about an increase in water accidents. Everyone can help to reduce the risks by following this advice:

- **go together**
- **avoid dangerous areas**
- **know what to do in an emergency**

If you wish to participate in a water-based sport, be sure to learn from the experts. Join a club and learn safe methods as well as how to use the equipment correctly.

Inland Water Safety

- avoid parking or driving cars near the water's edge
- keep children under careful supervision
- carry a lifeline with you
- stay away from gravel pits unless they have been turned into supervised recreation areas
- remember the side and floors of gravel pits and reservoirs can shelve very suddenly; they may also have steep, slippery or unsafe edges
- take care when near flooded foundations and excavations on building sites
- keep away from locks unless you are in a boat
- stay away from polluted water
- keep away from farm slurry pits
- remember to tell someone where you are going and when you will return

RIVER WEIR

CANAL LOCK

GRAVEL PIT

2

Safety by Canals, Rivers and Lakes

It is forbidden by law to swim in locks and canals. There are many dangers associated with boats, polluted water and changing water levels. Furthermore swimming in rivers and lakes is dangerous and unpredictable. Avoid swimming in these areas, unless approved lifeguard cover is available and the waters are considered safe enough for public use. If you have to enter the water:

- avoid standing on an overhanging bank
- observe the strength and direction of a current before entering
- check the depth of water before entering
- enter cold water slowly
- beware of boats using the waterway
- enter the water at the widest point, use a pole to feel your way, lean against the current
- lie flat in deep mud, spread your weight and move using a slow arm and leg action
- move slowly when caught in weeds using a sculling action
- swim at an angle to the current

Take note of warning signs, avoid murky or polluted water and always stay close to others. The cold, dangerous water conditions and unexpected incidents involving boats are all potential killers. Stay safe!

RIVER SIGNS

CANAL SIGN

RIVER SCENE

Lifesaving

Weil's Disease

Rivers, ponds and canals may be infected with a bacterium which can cause Weil's disease. Most of the time Weil's disease may take the form of a chill or possibly resemble an attack of flu. Sometimes it can be a serious illness requiring hospital treatment.

- if you fall ill with symptoms, after swimming, particularly within three weeks, then visit your doctor immediately
- explain where and when you have been swimming and request a special blood test for Weil's disease

2

Safety when Fishing

When you decide to go fishing, prepare thoroughly and wear suitable clothing and footwear. Anyone who goes fishing should possess a good knowledge of water safety and survival swimming. Always remember to:

- leave word of where you are going and your expected time of return
- fish in the company of at least one other person
- stay away from sloping and slippery rocks
- look for secure footholds
- check for hidden rocks and sudden drop offs when wading
- watch for changes in the weather
- stay away from steep, weak or crumbling banks
- watch the incoming tide to avoid being cut off from land

WARNING SIGN

RIVER FISHING SCENE

SURFING! NO SWIMMING!

DANGER! NO SWIMMING!

CAUTION! TAKE CARE!

CALM WATER! TAKE CARE!

ONLY SWIM HERE!

Safety in the Sea

Swimming in the sea can be dangerous. Care is needed to ensure that the chosen site is supervised and suitable for swimming. Alcohol has been a contributory factor in many swimming drownings as it has an adverse effect on the body and the ability to make reasonable judgements. Hot weather and holidays seem to encourage individuals to attempt the impossible.

- get advice about bathing conditions
- find out where and when it is safe to swim
- avoid drinking alcohol before swimming
- note the location of the nearest telephone and first aid point
- keep clear of surfboards, boats and natural hazards
- avoid boating and surfing areas marked by **black and white flags**
- stay on land when the **red flag** is flying
- take care when the **yellow flag** is flying (the water is not calm)
- take care when the **green flag** is flying (the water is calm but not safe)
- swim between the **red over yellow flags** where lifeguards patrol
- swim parallel to and not away from the shore
- avoid drifting away from the swimming area
- be aware of others in the water
- swim diagonally across the current to safety, as struggling against a current can be exhausting
- signal for help if you get into difficulty
- gain an understanding of the dangers of cold water, tides and currents
- remember that cold water quickly affects stamina
- get out of the water as soon as you feel cold or conditions become dangerous
- beware of a rising tide, as you can easily become stranded on sand banks or rocks
- beware of a falling tide which can easily pull you out to sea
- keep inflatable dinghies on a fixed line
- be aware of the dangers of entering the water after sunbathing

SAFETY IN THE SEA

Safety when Boating

Before going on the water, you should check your equipment carefully and ensure that you know what you are doing. At the very least, you should follow these guidelines:

- learn to swim
- check you boat and equipment regularly
- learn from the experts
- go out with someone experienced
- leave word of where you are going and when you expect to return
- follow the boat traffic rules
- know the limitations of your boat
- check the weather conditions
- keep all equipment stowed securely
- carry flares and emergency signals
- wear a lifejacket displaying the kite mark, make sure it fits and is fastened securely
- take appropriate clothing for changes in the weather
- keep the boat away from swimming areas, rocks, weirs and other craft
- keep a look out for bad weather warning signs, such as:
  - clouds building up to windward (upwind)
  - gusting winds and increased wind force
  - waves growing bigger
  - white caps appearing
- head for shore if bad weather threatens
- learn and practise capsize and man overboard drills
- stay with the boat in an emergency

Safety Supervision for Group Activities

When organising group activities, the following guidelines should be followed. Use an area which is properly supervised by qualified lifeguards. If a swimming area has to be established, you should:

- define the boundaries (using ropes with floats or human markers at regular intervals)
- remove all possible hazards or clearly mark them
- fence off danger areas
- provide trained lifeguards and a rescue craft for safety cover
- follow the guidelines given earlier in this chapter and ensure that the lifeguards on duty have provided you with a written copy of their NOP and EAP (see below) before the activity starts

2

WIND SURFING ACTIVITY

BE SAFE!
Learn from the experts! Addresses of major swimming, safety and sailing organisations can be found at the back of this book.

SAFETY SIGNS

WARNING!
Only qualified
and experienced
lifeguards should
supervise aquatic
activities.

Safety and Emergency Procedures for Aquatic Activities

Thorough preparation is needed if you are organising or arranging supervision of aquatic activities. Wherever you are and whatever you are doing you should have established clear, carefully planned and well documented operating procedures and emergency plans. These procedures and plans should be updated regularly and displayed prominently or handed to all supervisors or users of the facility or water area.

The RLSS UK Rescue Test for Teachers of Swimming or the National Pool or Beach Lifeguard Qualifications should be held by supervising staff in accordance with the rules and regulations of the aquatic facility. Specialist training and updating of awards is required every twenty four months.

Normal Operating Procedures (NOP)

For every supervised aquatic activity or environment, whether indoors or outdoors, you should develop a written policy and set of guidelines for your day-to-day working procedures. This document is commonly referred to as the NOP or Normal Operating Procedures and should contain the following details:

- plan of the aquatic area or facility
  including details of potential hazards, access points, information points, location of public rescue equipment, safety information
- potential risk factors
- supervision requirements
  including best observation points, communication procedures, back-up agencies (police, ambulance etc), procedures for designating and changing supervisors, minimum number of supervisors required, daily routines and duties, length and times of duties, qualifications required, fitness and skills required, uniform and personal equipment requirements
- rescue and first aid equipment requirements
  including checklist, specification, inspection and maintenance of equipment
- emergency provision
  including vehicles, water craft, telephones, radios, equipment
- emergency procedures (see EAP)
  including roles and responsibilities in an emergency
- incident recording and reporting
  including where, when and how to record and report
- public relations
  including dealing with users of the facility
- review procedures
  including monitoring effectiveness of NOP

Lifesaving

Developing an Emergency Action Plan (EAP)

For every supervised aquatic activity or environment you should prepare an emergency action plan, which will be followed by all supervising staff in the event of an emergency. It should include information on each of the following:

- location of the nearest telephone
- list of names, addresses and telephone numbers of support agencies
- how to telephone for help in an emergency
- transport and driver available for travelling to doctor or hospital
- location and content of first aid kit
- name of qualified first aid personnel on site
- location and types of rescue equipment
- identification, location and use of emergency signals
- statement of emergency procedures
- emergency action to be taken
- roles and responsibilities
- aftercare procedures
- methods of reporting and recording incidents

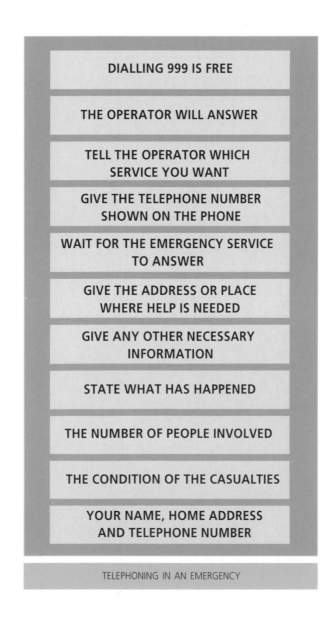

DIALLING 999 IS FREE

THE OPERATOR WILL ANSWER

TELL THE OPERATOR WHICH SERVICE YOU WANT

GIVE THE TELEPHONE NUMBER SHOWN ON THE PHONE

WAIT FOR THE EMERGENCY SERVICE TO ANSWER

GIVE THE ADDRESS OR PLACE WHERE HELP IS NEEDED

GIVE ANY OTHER NECESSARY INFORMATION

STATE WHAT HAS HAPPENED

THE NUMBER OF PEOPLE INVOLVED

THE CONDITION OF THE CASUALTIES

YOUR NAME, HOME ADDRESS AND TELEPHONE NUMBER

TELEPHONING IN AN EMERGENCY

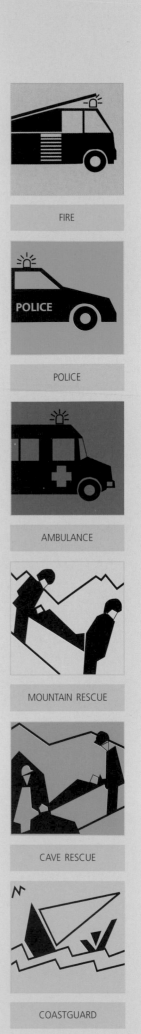

FIRE

POLICE

AMBULANCE

MOUNTAIN RESCUE

CAVE RESCUE

COASTGUARD

Public Rescue and Safety Equipment

Most local authorities and bodies responsible for open water facilities, such as rivers, lakes and reservoirs, now provide a variety of different rescue and safety equipment for public use in the case of an emergency. The most common are:

- warning signs
- life rings
- life buoys
- throwing ropes
- reaching poles
- telephones
- first aid kits

2

Training and Assessing Water Safety & Accident Prevention

Check your understanding by answering the questions opposite. Join a recognised lifesaving or lifeguarding club to develop your skills and knowledge further.

Training

You will need to participate in a wide range of aquatic activities under experienced supervision. You should learn to recognise different conditions and safety procedures. You should visit different open water environments. You should memorise the essential elements of aquatic accident prevention and start to promote water safety in your local community.

Assessing

You should assess your skills and knowledge on a regular basis by taking one or more of the RLSS UK teacher assessed water safety awards or by attempting to gain a major lifesaving award containing externally assessed water safety and rescue elements.

WATER ENTHUSIASTS

LIFE BUOY

Checking your Understanding of Water Safety

The following questions are designed to check your knowledge and understanding of water safety and accident prevention, as described in this chapter. Alongside each question is the relevant page reference.

WATER SAFETY!

2

Summary

Water safety & accident prevention depend on ensuring high standards of care, safety and supervision in and around water. You should follow the guidelines outlined in this chapter, be aware of the dangers when out and about and encourage your friends, family and local community to learn how to prevent accidents in water.

2

ACCIDENT PREVENTION SIGN

Swimming & Diving

3

Introduction to Swimming & Diving

This chapter provides information on the swimming and diving skills required for lifesaving. On the following pages you will find information about:

- swimming fitness
- front crawl and breast stroke
- side stroke and lifesaving backstroke
- sculling and treading water
- surface dives and swimming underwater
- entries and exits
- swimming equipment
- health and safety when swimming
- training and assessing swimming strokes

All lifesavers should understand the importance of mastering these swimming skills. Whilst there is a big difference between swimming in the local pool and being able to swim safely in open water, a competent swimmer is more likely to be a safer swimmer. In addition, knowledge, judgement and fitness are all needed to become a competent lifesaver.

Practise regularly; learn to swim competently in a variety of conditions; maintain a high level of fitness and stay within reach of safety whenever possible.

Swimming Fitness

Fitness and stamina are essential elements in the make-up of a competent lifesaver. To reach and maintain a satisfactory level of fitness you must exercise regularly, with appropriate amounts of work for sufficient duration. Research has shown that the physically fit lifesaver can:

- get to safety or to a casualty quickly
- avoid getting into difficulty
- complete rescues successfully over various distances
- tow casualties effectively over long distances
- maintain confidence, alertness and personal safety

A good swimming fitness programme will be based on the F.I.T.T. principle:

- **Frequency**
- **Intensity**
- **Time**
- **Type**

Frequency

Frequency is how often you undertake exercise. The frequency of your training sessions will depend on your commitment to your exercise programme as well as to your specific aims and objectives.

Intensity

Intensity is how hard you work when you are exercising. This is the hardest element to assess and control. Results are best when you maintain your training at a specific, beneficial level; working at a low level may be suitable for recovery, working at a high intensity may be difficult to maintain.

Time

Time is how long you spend exercising during each session. This will include your warm up, main activity and warm down. Your exercise session may last for a variable amount of time but should be broken up into sections to allow you to gain maximum benefit from the session.

Type

Type is what kind of exercise you do, whether aerobic or anaerobic, swimming long or short distances or varying the content and structure of your exercise programme.

Planning your Exercise Programme

Your exercise programme may be planned by a swimming trainer or coach, or if this is not possible, you should be able to find suitable books on swimming training and fitness in your local library or bookshop (a list of suggested titles appears in the bibliography at the back of this book). In brief, the main components of a safe and effective swimming training session are:

- flexibility and stretching exercises
- warm up swim
- main exercise activity
- warm down swim

Flexibility and Stretching Exercises

Flexibility and stretching exercises help to improve your range of movement in the water and reduce the risk of injury. They should be done slowly and gently, avoiding any pain or discomfort.

AQUA-FITNESS!

Warm Up

A warm up is designed to prepare your body for exercise. It should increase the blood flow and muscle temperature and help you to adjust to the exercise session. A good warm up will help prevent injury.

Main Activity

The main exercise activity should enable you to perform a sustained physical activity that requires additional effort by your heart and lungs to meet the increased demands from your muscles for oxygen (aerobic exercise).

Warm Down

A warm down should be the last part of your training session and should enable your heart rate and blood pressure to return to their initial levels. If done sensibly, it will help you to recover and prevent muscle injury.

3

Swimming Strokes

In rescue and survival, the strong swimmer has a great advantage. The following factors will affect the strokes selected for any lifesaving situation:

Resistance

The effectiveness of a stroke is adversely affected by resistance particularly when your body position in the water is poor, you are wearing clothing which increases drag or there are eddies and currents in the water.

Speed

Swimming speed is most likely to be maintained when resistance is low and the chosen stroke offers economical and effective movement; front crawl is a fast, generally economical stroke providing low water resistance.

Propulsion

Strokes which provide strong and effective propulsion are essential in rescue and survival situations. These strokes often make use of a glide phase, such as breast stroke and sidestroke, and are suited to a range of situations.

Energy

Energy is saved when strokes are swum slowly and the limbs are not lifted out of the water during recovery, such as in breast stroke, sidestroke and lifesaving backstroke.

Vision

In many rescue situations, you will need to observe both the direction of travel and the casualty and so will want to choose a stroke where the head is kept out of the water.

Lifesaving Strokes

There are four main swimming strokes suitable for rescue and survival purposes:

- **front crawl**
- **breast stroke**
- **side stroke**
- **lifesaving backstroke**

Back crawl and butterfly - the other two main strokes - are unsuitable for a number of reasons. Back crawl allows no vision in the direction of travel and is not effective in rough water, whilst butterfly is very strenuous requiring both arms to recover simultaneously over the water whilst the head and shoulders have to lift for breathing.

Lifesaving

FRONT CRAWL

BREAST STROKE

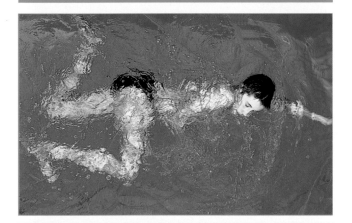

SIDE STROKE

LIFESAVING BACKSTROKE

3

Front Crawl
- fastest stroke for approaching a casualty or escaping from danger
- allows unrestricted vision when swum head up

3

Technique
You can adapt your front crawl technique to suit your physical ability as well as different swimming and lifesaving situations. While one arm cycle to a six beat leg kick is most commonly used, you may prefer the less tiring two or four beat kick particularly when swimming long distances.

Body Position
- lie on your front, keeping your body flat, streamlined, relaxed and as horizontal as possible
- keep the waterline between the eyes and hairline
- adjust you body position by raising or lowering the head
- make use of lateral roll to assist your stroke and breathing

FRONT CRAWL BODY POSITION

Leg Action
The leg kick maintains your body in a stable, streamlined position and helps with forward propulsion.

- kick rhythmically up and down, from the hips
- keep your legs relaxed, bending slightly at the knees
- keep your ankles flexible and loose
- flex your feet with the toes pointed and turned slightly inwards
- allow your heels to just churn the surface of the water

FRONT CRAWL LEG ACTION

Arm Action
Both arms should move in a continuous alternating movement with one arm engaged in the underwater stroke as the other arm recovers over the water (the arm action will provide most of the stroke's forward propulsion).

- with your arm extended, place one hand in the water in advance of the shoulder, pitched at a 45 degree angle (thumb first) in order to avoid taking air bubbles with it
- sweep the hand backwards through an S-shaped pattern with the elbow bending progressively until half-way through the stroke (by which point your elbow should be set at approximately 90 degrees with the hand under the body)

Lifesaving

- hold the elbow higher than the hand (keeping it sideways to prevent the hand "slipping" through the water)
- straighten the elbow, half way through the sweep, by pushing the hand backwards and outwards past the hips and extending the arm
- throughout the sweep, move your hand in a sculling action as it pitches inwards across the body and outwards as your arm extends
- recover your arm over the water in a relaxed way using the momentum created during the underwater phase
- during the recovery phase over the water, keep your elbow high with the hand close to the body and the water surface

Breathing
Breathe in during each arm cycle, as described below:

- roll your head with the natural rotation of your body to assist breathing
- either choose to breathe in on one side of the body only
- or breathe on each side alternately (bi-lateral breathing)

Breathing in
- turn your head to the side to breathe in
- start breathing in as your arm recovers over the water
- breathe in through your mouth or mouth and nose

Breathing out
- either start breathing out immediately the mouth is under-water (trickle breathing)
- or breathe out explosively just before you turn your head to breathe in again (explosive breathing)

Timing
The alternating arm recovery over the water takes less time than the stroke underwater so one arm should enter as the other is about halfway through its underwater stroke. Timing in front crawl varies from swimmer to swimmer and according to the situation. Variations include one arm cycle to six leg beats, four leg beats or two leg beats.

Vision
Raise your head above the water at least every five seconds, to assist in observing the casualty during the approach swim to a casualty.

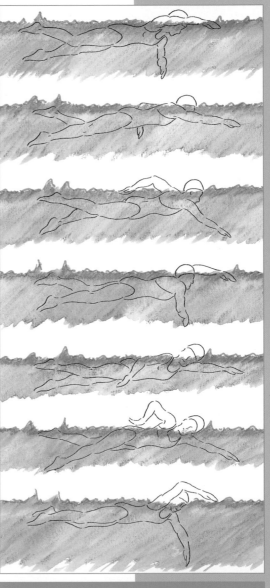

FRONT CRAWL SEQUENCE

Breast Stroke

- good endurance stroke when performed slowly
- can be adapted well to swimming underwater
- allows uninterrupted breathing if the head is high above water
- allows unrestricted forward vision if the head is held above water
- the head may be turned away from wind and waves

Technique

Styles of breast stroke vary considerably. For survival swimming you should maintain a slow, relaxed style. For rescue purposes you may need to use a faster stroke, while still maintaining a smooth style.

Body Position

- keep your body as flat as possible in the water to reduce resistance
- raise your head towards the end of the arm sweep to reduce resistance
- recover your legs by bending at the knees and hips and keeping the hips high in the water
- keep your heels close to, but not breaking, the surface

Leg Action

The breaststroke leg action is a simultaneous symmetrical action. It provides exceptional forward propulsion , is excellent for survival and rescue purposes and can be used on front or back as well as for treading water.

- recover your legs from an extended position by drawing your heels towards your bottom
- keep your ankles dorsi-flexed (toes pointed towards the shins) with your knees and feet together at first (although they may separate to about shoulder width as the knees fully flex)
- before starting the kick, turn your feet outwards keeping your ankles dorsi-flexed (allow the inside of your feet and legs to face backwards providing the surface area for the backward thrust)
- start the kick by thrusting your feet apart and backwards with the heels tracing a circular pattern as they accelerate smoothly backwards
- bring the feet together just after the legs straighten

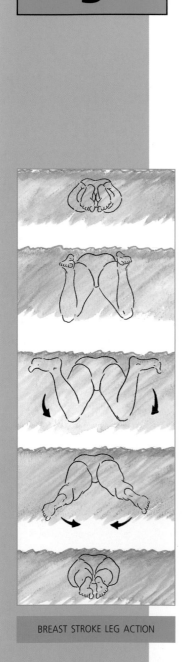

BREAST STROKE LEG ACTION

Lifesaving

Arm Action

The breast stroke arm action is simultaneous and symmetrical. Start with your arms fully extended in front of your body:

- press your palms downwards and outwards diagonally, pitching your hands at a 45 degree angle
- when your hands are just beyond shoulder line width, bend the elbows and accelerate your hands towards the centre line of your body
- pitch your hands at 45 degrees with the palms facing inwards
- maintain a high elbow position until the hands finish their inwards movement
- glide your hands forward to full arm extension with the palms pitched inwards

Breathing

- breathe during every stroke
- lift your head by extending your neck at the end of the arm sweep
- breathe in when your face is clear of the water
- lower your head and face to the water just before the arms return to full extension
- breathe out when your face is under or in line with the water surface

Timing

The most commonly used sequence is:

- *GLIDE - PULL - BREATHE - KICK - GLIDE*

A glide, after each kick and before the next arm sweep, provides a period of rest and takes full advantage of the propulsive phase of the stroke.

Keep your body extended for the glide. You can hold this position for varying lengths of time depending on the conditions or activity being undertaken.

Vision

For rescue and survival purposes, you may need to hold your head above water for long periods to keep land or a casualty in sight.

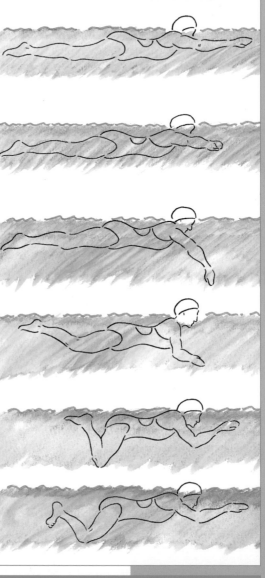

BREAST STROKE SEQUENCE

Side Stroke

- demands relatively small energy output at low speed
- leg action provides great propulsive power for towing
- breathing in is not interrupted
- head may be held out of the water if necessary
- vision ahead and behind is satisfactory
- possible to swim the stroke on either side of the body
- can provide protection for the face in choppy water
- suitable for towing purposes
- useful in survival and rescue situations

3

SIDE STROKE BODY POSITION

Technique

The stroke may be performed on either side using an othodox or inverted scissor kick.

Body Position

- stretch the body out on the side in a relaxed and streamlined position, remaining as horizontal as possible
- rest one side of the head in the water

Leg Action

The four phases of the scissor kick are bend, open, kick and glide.

SIDE STROKE LEG ACTION

- recover the legs simultaneously in a relaxed manner by bending at the hips and knees with the legs and feet together
- open the legs horizontally by moving the upper leg forward and the lower leg backward
- keep the ankle of the top leg dorsi-flexed (toes drawn up towards the shins) and the ankle of the lower leg plantar-flexed (toes pointed)
- open the legs wide, kick backwards and bring the feet together (you should feel water pressure against the sole of the front foot and the upper surface of the back foot)
- hold the legs together with toes pointed for a short glide

When the top leg is moved forward, it is an orthodox scissor kick. When the bottom leg is opened forward, it is an inverted scissor kick. Your swimming ability as well as the conditions will dictate which method is best suited to each survival and rescue situation.

Arm Action

- extend your lower arm just below the surface and beyond your head in the glide phase of the stroke
- extend your upper arm along the side of your body with the hand just below the surface

Lower Arm

- sweep backwards along a curved pathway with your elbow bending progressively until your hand is level with your shoulders and your elbow bent at approximately 90 degrees
- pass your hand close to your chin with your wrist bent back (hyper-extended) to enable the hand to push forward to the glide position with minimum resistance

Upper Arm

- move your upper hand from your thigh to a position just below your chin, keep your hand close to your body to minimise resistance
- push your hand strongly through to your thigh to assist propulsion
- keep your arm extended at your thigh for the glide

3

Breathing

Breathing in should take place during the out sweep of the bottom arm. If necessary, the head may turn slightly face upward to keep the mouth clear of the water.

Timing

The sequence of the stroke is:

- *GLIDE - PULL - BREATHE - KICK - GLIDE*

Vision

For rescue purposes, hold your head slightly above the water, turning to watch and reassure a casualty either during an approach swim or whilst towing.

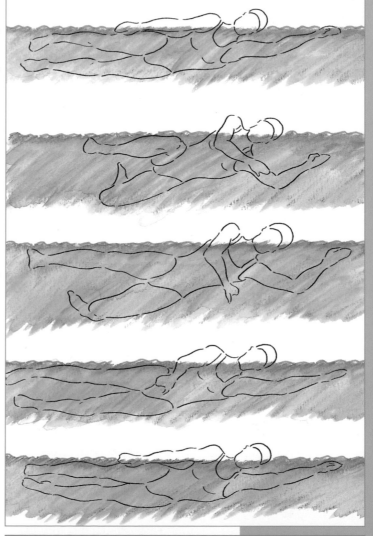

SIDE STROKE SEQUENCE

Lifesaving Backstroke

- breathing is not interrupted
- useful endurance stroke for survival
- head may be held out of the water if necessary
- useful for towing, especially when two hands are required to hold a casualty
- useful for carrying objects in deep water
- allows unrestricted vision except in the direction of travel
- can be performed with a variety of kicks (breast stroke, eggbeater)
- arm can be held out of the water to signal for help
- ·useful in difficult conditions
- hands can assist with propulsion

Technique

The important elements of lifesaving backstroke may be seen from studying the sequence of illustrations. It uses a simultaneous and symmetrical arm and leg action.

Body Position

- stretch out on your back in a streamlined position with both ears in the water
- keep your hips close to, but slightly below, the surface of the water
- adjust your body position by tilting your head

Leg Action

Variations of the inverted breast stroke leg kick are usually preferred for this stroke; although the eggbeater leg kick is sometimes used.

- fully extend the legs during the glide phase with the toes pointed (ankles plantar flexed)
- recover the legs by bending at the knees
- avoid bending at the hips as this will cause the hips to drop and so increase resistance
- as the feet drop, spread your knees and feet slightly and curl your toes towards your shins (ankles dorsi-flexed)
- when the bend in the knees reaches about 90 degrees, turn the feet outwards keeping your ankles dorsi-flexed (this position is essential to the success of the kick)
- start the kick by thrusting your feet apart with your heels tracing a circular pattern as they travel backwards
- bring your feet together as the legs straighten

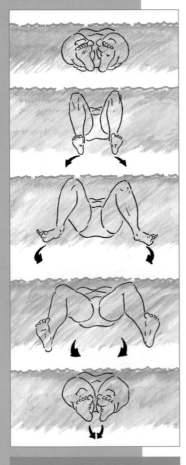

LIFESAVING BACKSTROKE LEG ACTION

Lifesaving

Water pressure should be felt on the insides and soles of the feet during the kick. The feet should accelerate smoothly, reaching maximum speed only in the final stage of the kick. Knee extension provides the speed and so the knees should not complete their extension until the feet are coming together at the end of the kick.

Arm Action

- adopt a streamlined position with your arms fully extended by your side and your hands close to your thighs
- draw your hands simultaneously to your shoulders, below the surface, by bending your arms at the elbows and keeping your hands close to your body
- push your hands sideways with the palms facing backwards
- perform a strong sweep, with your elbows pointing straight downwards to prevent your hands "slipping" through the water
- as your hands pass your shoulders, straighten your arms and push strongly towards your thighs
- alternatively a short sculling action may be used (see section on sculling)

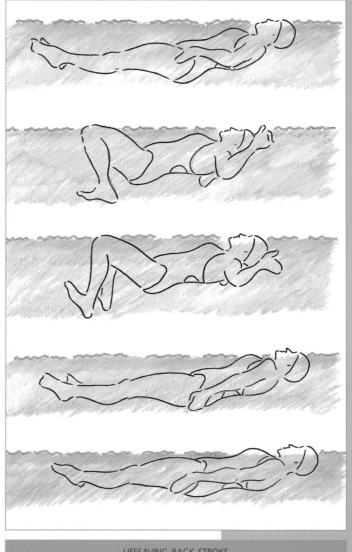

Breathing

Keep your face clear of the water. Breathe in as your legs and arms recover, breathe out as you complete the kick.

Timing

The sequence for the stroke is:

- *GLIDE - BREATHE - PULL & KICK TOGETHER - GLIDE*

From the glide position, your arms and legs should recover at the same time. The propulsive arm and leg actions also occur simultaneously. Glide between strokes to make maximum use of the propulsive phase.

Vision

For survival and rescue purposes, particularly when towing a casualty towards land, you will need to turn your head every five to ten seconds to check your direction of travel. Lifesaving backstroke provides excellent observation of the casualty at all times.

LIFESAVING BACK STROKE

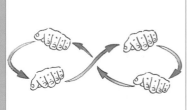

Sculling

Sculling is a difficult yet important skill which can be used in many situations by the lifesaver. It requires practice but should be learned by lifesavers of all ages and abilities. You can use sculling to develop your stroke technique and it is particularly helpful when swimming through weeds.

Stationary Sculling
- lie in a flat streamlined position on your back
- hold your arms straight by the sides of your body, palms facing downwards
- sweep your hands outwards and inwards in a figure of eight movement keeping the hands on the same level and the palms facing down
- keep your palms slightly cupped below the surface with the fingers together
- movement should be smooth, firm and continuous

Sculling Feet First
- flex your wrists, fingers pointing down to the bottom and your palms facing towards your head
- adopt the same basic sculling action as described above

Sculling Head First
- bend your wrists backwards, fingers pointing upwards and palms facing towards your feet
- keep your body flat, streamlined and fully extended
- adopt the same basic sculling action as above

SCULLING HAND SEQUENCE

SCULLING

Treading Water

All lifesavers need to be able to tread water. The skill is valuable in both rescue and survival situations. You should learn to tread water whenever you want to keep your head above the surface in deep water. With your body in an upright position, use one of the following leg actions:

- breast stroke kick
- scissor kick
- cycling action
- eggbeater kick

Keep your arms below the surface and use a relaxed sculling action.

Eggbeater Kick

A powerful treading water action is required (this is the most efficient method of lifting the body high out of the water and is very useful for deep water resuscitation and towing):

- sit in the water, back straight, knees spread apart and the thighs almost parallel to the surface
- drive the legs in an alternating circular pattern, rotating at the knees
- as one leg drives, the other recovers
- for travelling purposes, the leg and body positions are altered slightly to allow the feet to drive downward in a direction opposite to the line of travel

TREADING WATER USING BREAST STROKE ACTION

EGGBEATER KICK

EGGBEATER KICK

Surface Diving

Extended Feet First Surface Dive

You should use an extended feet first surface dive when you are searching in unclear water and escaping from underneath upturned boats. You can also use it when you need to submerge quickly feet first.

- swim to the appropriate point to submerge
- take a deep breath
- kick vigorously and push downwards with both hands in order to raise your body in the water
- point your toes and swing both hands upwards until they are together above your head
- by holding your body upright and your legs together you will be driven vertically downwards
- once beneath the surface, scull with your hands to keep your body submerged, whilst feeling with your feet for possible hazards

Controlled Feet First Surface Dive

You should use a controlled feet first surface dive when a slower, more controlled descent is required.

- bring your body into the treading water position
- stop treading water, bring your legs together straight and point your toes
- use your hands in an upward scooping action to propel the body downwards in a slow, controlled manner

FEET FIRST SURFACE DIVE

3

Lifesaving

Head First Surface Dive

You should use a head first surface dive when a casualty has submerged and must be recovered as soon as possible. This dive can be used to escape from danger, though it should never be used in unknown conditions.

- swim to a position above but just short of the object to be recovered
- take a breath before diving
- without losing momentum, drop your head, pull your arms to a position level with your shoulders and bend at the hips (breaststroke approach)
- or drop your head and drive downwards forcibly with the leading arm (front crawl approach)
- as your upper body submerges, pull your arms back towards your face and lift both legs clear of the water to vertical position
- the weight of the legs above the water will provide the main force for descent; although further depth and change of direction can be gained by swimming underwater

HEAD FIRST SURFACE DIVE

Swimming Underwater

You may need to swim underwater to recover a submerged object or to escape from danger on the surface.

- **eithe**r use a breast stroke arm and leg action (in clear water only)
- keep your chin close to your chest and recover your arms close to your body
- **or** use a breast stroke arm action and front crawl kick
- extend your arms beyond your head to guard against submerged obstructions
- open your eyes to see where you are going!

The pressure of water increases with depth. A depth of more than 1.5 metres is sufficient to cause pain and damage to the swimmer's middle ear, ear drums and sinuses, unless the pressure is equal to the pressure of the surrounding water (this can even occur in shallow water for those with colds or sinus problems). Holding your nose, exhaling through the nostrils, swallowing and moving the jaw are all ways of equalising the pressure.

SWIMMING UNDERWATER

WARNING!
Do not take deep or repeated breaths before submerging. Hyperventilation may cause sudden and un-expected loss of consciousness.

SLIDE IN ENTRY

STEP IN ENTRY

Entries and Exits

Slide In Entry

You should use a slide in entry when the depth and underwater conditions are unknown. Your entry should be controlled and safe allowing the feet to feel for unseen obstacles below the surface.

- establish a firm body position by sitting on the bank with your feet in the water
- feel for obstacles with your feet
- lower your body gently, taking the weight on the hands

Step In

You can use a step in entry when the water is clear, the depth is known and you can see the bottom is free from obstacles.

- look at the point of entry
- step gently off the edge
- keep your knees and legs slightly flexed as your feet touch the bottom

Compact Jump

You should use a feet first compact jump when you need to enter deep water from a height of more than one metre.

- place both arms across your upper body
- step off with one foot leading, bring your legs together and keep them straight
- keep your body vertical, streamlined and protected
- once underwater tuck or pike the body to check downward movement (the arms and legs can also be used to assist in braking)

COMPACT JUMP

Lifesaving

Straddle Entry

You can use a straddle entry when you are entering deep water from a low height and you need to watch a casualty in difficulty. It must not be used from heights above one metre or for entries into unknown or shallow water.

- step out from a standing position, aiming for distance
- extend one leg forward and the other leg backward with the knees slightly bent
- lean forward
- extend the arms sideways and slightly forwards (palms downwards)
- hold your head still and look forward
- on entry press down with your arms and scissor your legs, keeping your head above water

STRADDLE ENTRY

WARNING
It is dangerous to dive into shallow water. You should never attempt to dive into water which is less than 1.5 metres deep.

Shallow Dive

You can use a shallow dive when the water is clear, the bottom can be seen and the depth is known.

- stand on the side with your toes curled over the edge
- look down and forward in the direction of travel
- bend your knees and use your arms to help gain forward momentum
- push off as far as possible out over the water
- enter with your body almost horizontal to the water (extending your arms and legs)
- keep your head between your arms, with your eyes looking towards the water
- keep your body straight and streamlined
- commence swimming after entry by raising your head slightly to bring you to the surface

Health and Safety when Diving

- learn how to dive properly
- follow these safety rules at all times
- do not wear ear plugs
- obey no diving signs
- check the water depth
- never dive into shallow or murky water
- dive only when supervised and always look before entering the water
- swim away from a diving area

SHALLOW DIVE SEQUENCE

Deep and Shallow Exits

- place both hands on the side, shoulder width apart
- raise your body as high as possible to clear the water
- kick your legs and push down with your arms
- lean forward, place one foot or knee over the edge and climb out

Wearing a personal flotation device makes this exit more difficult. Practise climbing out from a variety of locations and depths.

Health and Safety when Swimming

In addition to the advice given above regarding the safety aspects of swimming, entering the water, surface diving and swimming underwater, as a swimmer you should:

- maintain a high level of personal hygiene
- seek professional medical advice if you are feeling unwell or are injured
- avoid swimming if you are suffering from any of the following:
- infectious diseases
- open wounds
- coughs, colds and related infections such as catarrh and sinusitis
- sore eyes
- ear infections

Most of all you should adopt a common sense approach to leisure and training activities, use of the facilities and to your behaviour in and around water.

DEEP WATER EXIT

3

Swimming Equipment

A wide variety of equipment is available to support swimming activities. The most common and useful are listed below:

- **arm bands** - for supporting weak swimmers in the water
- **hoops** - for swimming underwater and diving
- **sinking objects** - for surface diving
- **inflatable tubes and rings** - for support, buoyancy and towing
- **kick boards or floats** - for support, buoyancy and swimming practices
- **pull-buoys** - for arm action practices
- **hand paddles** - for arm action practices
- **fins** - for underwater swimming and propulsion practices
- **anti-chlorine goggles** - for underwater vision and eye protection
- **masks & snorkels** - for underwater swimming and diving

3

Training and Assessing Swimming & Diving Skills

Answer the questions below to check your knowledge and understanding of swimming skills. Join a recognised lifesaving or lifeguard club to develop your skills and knowledge further.

Training

You should participate in a regular and carefully organised training programme which will enable you to improve and maintain high levels of fitness, stamina and performance in swimming. You should practise your swimming skills, under supervision, in different aquatic environments. You will need to improve aspects of your strokes by using specifically designed practices.

Assessing

You should test your swimming fitness and skills regularly through RLSS UK trainer assessed swimming awards or by attempting to gain one of the major lifesaving awards which includes externally assessed swimming fitness elements.

READY FOR SWIMMING

Checking your Understanding of Swimming & Diving

The following questions are designed to check your knowledge and understanding of swimming and diving, as described in this chapter; alongside each question you will find the relevant page reference.

Summary

Swimming is an effective means of keeping fit. The skills involved are fundamental to the development of competent survival and rescue skills. Practise regularly all the skills described in this chapter and ensure that you follow the safety guidelines for diving and swimming underwater. Further information on swimming strokes, teaching methods, games, drills and practices is available from RLSS UK, the ASA and STA (addresses at the back of this book).

CLIMBING OUT!

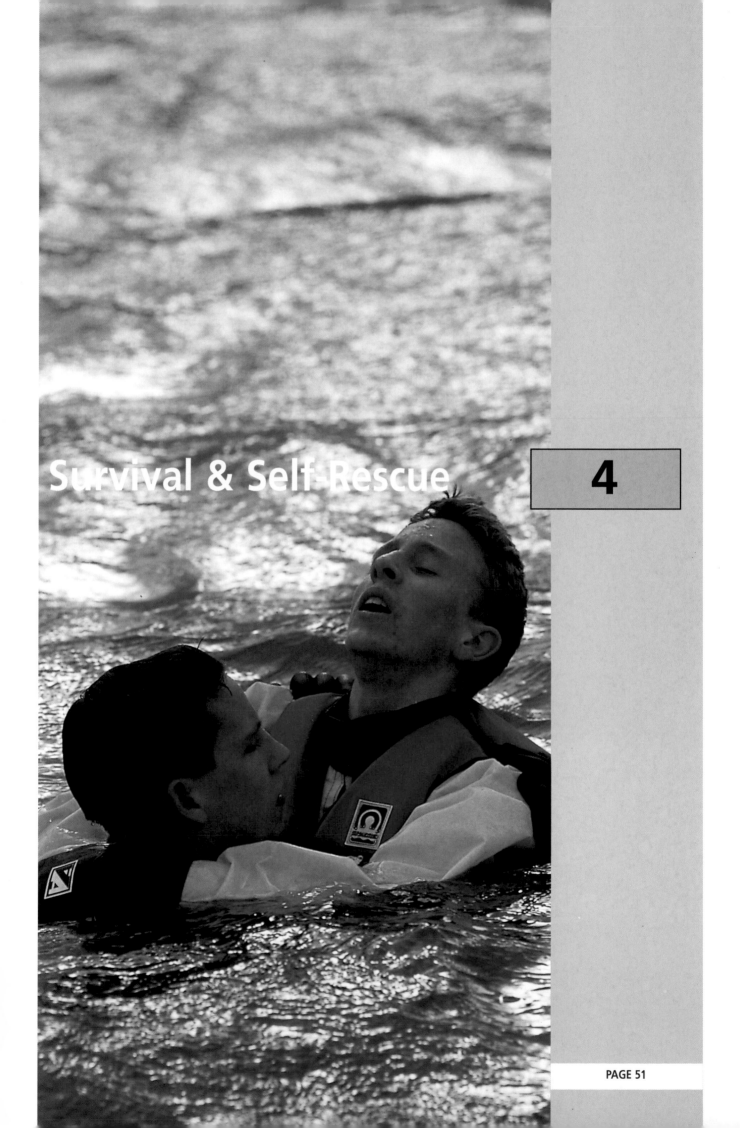

Survival & Self-Rescue

4

Introduction to Survival and Self-Rescue

This chapter provides details of the principles and skills of survival and self-rescue. On the following pages you will find information about:

SURVIVAL SITUATION

- survival principles in an emergency
- survival strategies in deep water
- survival floating and removal of clothing
- using lifejackets and buoyancy aids
- hypothermia and survival in cold water
- survival in tides and currents
- survival in dangerous situations

Survival is the ability to look after yourself and other people in an emergency and live to tell the tale! While the principles of personal and group survival in water are the same, they require careful consideration before they are applied in practice.

4

WARNING!
Open water is cold!
The risk of
hypothermia is
always present.

Survival Principles

In any survival or self-rescue situation, you need to develop an emergency plan which will assist you in coping with and surviving the experience. Such a plan is based on five main elements:

- assessment of the situation
- action based on this initial assessment
- reassessment of the situation after the initial action
- planning any follow-up action
- evaluating the success of our actions

Let us look at each of these areas in turn.

Assessment
You need to consider:

- temperature of the water
- distance from the shore
- ability to swim to safety
- possibility of receiving help
- weather and water conditions
- estimated survival time
- clothing to be worn
- availability of buoyant aids

Action
- employ the most effective method of survival or self-rescue for the situation

Lifesaving

Reassessment
- continue to check and reassess the action you have taken
- if conditions change you may need to change your decision and make further alterations to your plan

Aftercare and Support
You will need to consider:

- need for medical help
- how you will get help
- where you will obtain assistance
- whether the incident should be reported

Evaluation
Learn from your experiences. You should consider:

- how to avoid such a situation occurring in the future
- what needs to be done to prevent it happening to others
- whether warning or danger signs are needed
- how you would modify your actions in the future

SAFETY ON WATER

Survival Strategies in Deep Water
Survival in a deep water emergency depends on the individual's ability to use knowledge, judgement, skill and fitness to cope with the situation. It is important to remain calm and where possible consider the following procedures:

Pre-Entry
Before entering the water, check:

- lifejackets are being worn and are correctly fastened
- availability of assistance
- who is responsible for organising and assisting others
- number of persons in the group and their abilities
- availability of buoyancy and other aids
- environmental conditions
- removal of hazardous items of clothing
- method or means of survival thereafter

CAPSIZE!

ENTERING COLD WATER

Entry

Entries should be carried out calmly and with control.

- plan your entry carefully
- minimise risk and injury
- select the correct method of entry for conditions

Immersion

- use the H.E.L.P and HUDDLE survival methods
- float, scull or tread water in a relaxed manner
- put on or secure lifejacket
- hold on to buoyancy aid for support

If a number of people are in difficulty, you will need to decide whom to help. Usually the closest person should be secured first.

Personal Survival

Only swim when absolutely necessary. It is essential to conserve energy and body heat.

- think positively
- keep calm
- make a plan
- stay afloat
- hold onto a buoyant aid
- keep body and limbs submerged
- retain clothing
- swim slowly - if you have to move.
- change position and stroke regularly to lessen muscle fatigue
- keep your eyes open
- breathe regularly in a controlled manner
- attract attention by raising one arm above your head.

PERSONAL SURVIVAL

Group Survival

- appoint a leader
- keep together
- supervise the weaker swimmers
- use survival and buoyancy aids
- support each other (HUDDLE)
- avoid danger and tiring action
- encourage one another

HUDDLE

Signals in Emergency Situations

Recognise, learn and use these distress signals:

- red flares or orange smoke signals
- slow and repeated raising and lowering of an outstretched arm to the side
- waving a raised oar
- six blasts of a whistle at one minute intervals (international distress signal)

FLARE

RAISED ARM

Signalling for Help

- adopt a suitable floating, sculling or treading water position
- attract attention by raising one arm above your head
- shout for help

Conserve energy, stay where you are and wait calmly for assistance.

RAISED OAR

WHISTLE

Survival Skills

Fall In

When you fall into water unexpectedly:

- tuck the chin on the chest
- hold the top of the head with both hands protecting the face with the forearms
- press both elbows to the chest
- keep legs together with knees bent towards the chest

Survival Floating

When you need to conserve energy:

- lie in a horizontal, angled or vertical position with face clear of the water
- hold a buoyant aid to the chest
- motionless floating is a difficult skill, which is often easier to perform in salt water, where buoyancy is better than in fresh water

FALL IN ACTION

Removal of Clothing

Removal of layers of clothing reduces the ability of the body to retain heat and may quickly induce hypothermia and eventually loss of consciousness. When garments are too heavy or are restricting breathing, as a general rule, clothing should be removed from the feet upwards while treading water.

Shoes

- unlace with one hand
- bend your knees towards your head
- kick the shoes off while treading water (or ease the shoes off with the toes of the other foot)

Trousers/Skirt

- Undo at the waist, tuck your body and steadily pull off, submerge if necessary

T-Shirts and Sweaters

- Take one arm out at a time then roll up from the waist and lift clear over your head from the front

Coats and Shirts

- Unbutton and slip one arm out at a time (special care should be taken with synthetic items which may cling to the body while wet and restrict breathing)

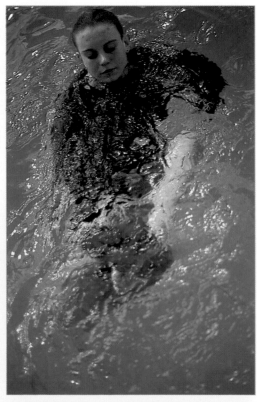

REMOVING TROUSERS IN WATER

Personal Flotation Devices (PFDs)

Personal flotation devices (PFDs) vary in uses and design and can be generally divided into two categories - lifejackets and buoyancy aids.

Lifejackets are worn on the body for the purpose of maintaining the wearer in a safe floating position. They are usually constructed with a buoyant collar and a pad of buoyant material next to the chest. This makes it difficult to swim any distance. Some lifejackets depend on air for buoyancy. They often remain deflated until a toggle is pulled or impact is made with water. Such jackets are usually carried on aircraft.

Buoyancy aids include the traditional buoyancy jacket which is worn on the body and intended for use in aquatic sports to assist flotation during short term immersion in cold waters. It is not designed to support any casualty, whether conscious or unconscious, in a fixed position. The material in a buoyancy aid is usually distributed evenly around the upper body making swimming much easier.

BSI KITE MARK

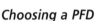

4

Choosing a PFD

- seek specialist advice
- look for a lifejacket carrying the British Standards Institution Kite Mark and manufactured to BSI specification 3595/81
- look for a buoyancy jacket manufactured to the Ship and Boat Builders National Federation specification (SBBNF/79)
- a PFD should fit comfortably, correctly and securely
- the buoyancy capacity should be adequate for the user's weight

Wearing a PFD

- become familiar with wearing a PFD
- practise using it in different situations, for example:
  - putting it on in the water as well as on land
  - sharing it as a flotation aid
  - getting in and out of the water wearing it
  - swimming in it
  - rolling over and submerging in it

Entry into Water Using a PFD

- slide in, jump feet first or roll in backwards
- hold the PFD securely, pulling hard down with both hands to prevent injury to the neck on hitting the water

PFD USERS

Cold Water Immersion and Hypothermia

Cold water immersion is a major factor in many drownings and rescues. It applies to emergency situations throughout the year. Details of the problems caused by sudden immersion in cold water and how to treat them are explained more fully in Chapter 7 and in the RLSS UK publication, 'Life Support'. This section briefly outlines the causes and effects of cold water immersion and hypothermia.

Causes of Hypothermia

The normal body temperature of a healthy person is about 36.9°C. Hypothermia occurs when the core body temperature (particularly the heart, lungs and brain) is lowered below 35°C. This may be caused by sudden immersion in cold water or by significant and unexpected differences in the temperature.

Effects of Hypothermia

When exposed to cold conditions, the human body reacts in the following ways as it's core temperature decreases:

37°C to 35°C

- shivering becomes intense and uncontrollable
- ability to perform complex tasks is impaired

35°C to 33°C

- violent shivering
- difficulty in speaking

33°C to 30°C

- shivering decreases and is replaced by muscular rigidity
- muscle co-ordination is affected producing erratic or jerky movements
- in most cases the casualty is still coherent
- thinking is less clear, general comprehension confused

30°C to 27°C

- unconsciousness
- no response to spoken word
- most reflexes cease to function
- heartbeat becomes erratic

Below 25°C

- failure of cardiac and respiratory centres in the brain
- death

CASUALTY IN COLD WATER

4

Lifesaving

Wind Chill Factor

In addition to cold water, the body may be dangerously cooled and chilled by the wind. The colder the air temperature, the greater the heat loss from the body. Hence, on a cold windy winter's day, someone participating in water sports may be at risk from both the effects of cold water and the wind.

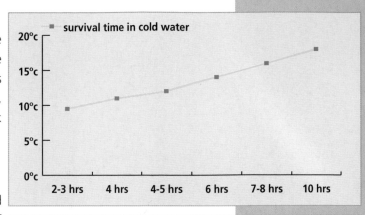

SURVIVAL TIME IN COLD WATER

Survival Time in Cold Water

Survival time varies according to body size and weight. The figures in this chart apply to an adult of average size. The survival time is linked to water temperature.

Sea Temperatures Around the British Isles

The sea temperatures shown in the chart below are typical of mid month temperatures away from the coast in the general area of the named location. In open sea there is very little variation between day and night. In summertime, sea temperatures close to the land will generally be warmer than indicated especially where the water is shallow or the incoming tide crosses the sandy beach at the end of a warm day. However during the winter the shallow water and river estuaries around the UK are usually colder than the temperatures shown below.

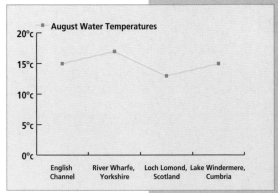

AVERAGE AUGUST WATER TEMPERATURES

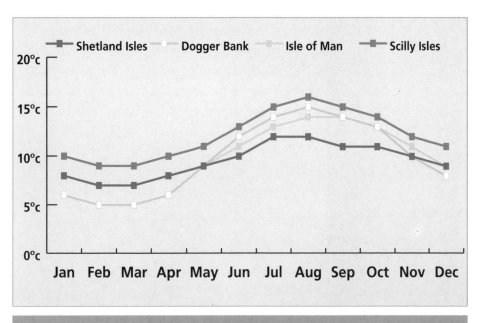

AVERAGE MID MONTH OFF SHORE SEA TEMPERATURES

Survival in Cold Water

This section explains how to survive in cold water for prolonged periods. The four key principles of survival in cold water are:

- **keep calm**
- **retain clothing**
- **float quietly**
- **tread water**

Swimming for Safety

If the shore or a boat is close by, swim slowly to that safer position and get out of the water. Remember the cold seriously affects co-ordination and stamina. In cold and rough conditions you would not get very far.

When you cannot swim to safety, it is essential that you conserve your energy and avoid sudden or prolonged movements. For these situations there are two tried and tested methods for surviving in cold water:

H.E.L.P. (Heat Escape Lessening Posture)

If you are wearing a lifejacket or PFD, the survival time can be increased sometimes by adopting the H.E.L.P. position. This position protects the core areas of the body which lose heat most quickly.

- keep your legs straight and together
- press both arms against your upper body
- keep your head out of the water

A number of different methods for conserving heat have been tried by casualties in cold water survival situations.

While previous methods have included tucking the legs up close to the chest and lying horizontally in the water, the technique illustrated has proved, in recent years, to be the most effective for conserving heat and energy over variable periods of time.

H.E.L.P. USING A LIFE BUOY

Paddington had never been in a bathroom before and while the water was running he made himself at home. First of all, he tried writing his new name in the steam on the mirror.

Then he used Mr Brown's shaving foam to draw a map of Peru on the floor. It wasn't until a drip landed on his head that he remembered what he was supposed to be doing.

Lifesaving

Huddle

The HUDDLE position is useful for small groups wearing lifejackets. It works on the same principle as the H.E.L.P. position by reducing the loss of body heat. Your group should:

- press the sides of their chests together
- press their groins and lower bodies together
- put their arms around each other's backs at waist level

A strong flotation aid can also be used satisfactorily for both H.E.L.P. and HUDDLE, when lifejackets are not available.

GROUP HUDDLE WEARING LIFEJACKETS

Without a Flotation Aid

Remove any heavy boots or coats but retain the rest of your clothing. Stay as still as possible by:

- **floating**
- **sculling**
- **treading water**

Floating is the best survival technique in this case as the other activities will increase the loss of body heat. However, care should be taken to keep the head above water as much as possible.

Remember if you find yourself in cold water

- keep calm
- float quietly, clinging where possible, to a buoyant aid.
- use H.E.L.P. to reduce the loss of heat from your body
- use the HUDDLE position when there is more than one person in the water
- even exceptionally strong swimmers may be overcome by shock and cold within very short distances, often as little as 50 metres
- do not remove clothing, except for very heavy overcoats and boots, even to make floats
- avoid immersing your head in the water

4

Survival in Tides and Currents

Currents can be present in a wide range of open water environments; although their formation and action varies from lakes to rivers to the sea. Many drownings and emergency situations occur through a lack of awareness of water currents.

While currents are often dangerous, they can also be used to assist with survival or rescue in an emergency. It is important that swimmers know how currents can help with survival or rescue.

River Currents

River currents are unpredictable. The flow wanders from shore to shore depending on such factors as:

- projecting headlands
- islands
- winding river course

SWIMMING AT AN ANGLE TO THE CURRENT

As a result, river currents rarely follow the contour of the river. Eddies (whirlpools in the water) and reverse currents which vary in strength may be found near the river bank or obstacles.

The strength of the current depends upon:

- volume of water
- width and depth of water
- rate of drop of river bed

If you ever have to swim in moving water, always remember to swim at an angle to the current.

Sea Currents

There are generally two types of sea currents:

- **tidal currents** are caused by the rise (flood) and fall (ebb) of the tide. They do not always flow in and out of the shore but may flow across or at an angle to the shore: particularly at the entrance to bays, inlets and river mouths.
- **runback currents** are caused by the backwash of waves and are usually strongest where the beach is steep. Inshore or side currents are produced by waves breaking over a sand bank or by waves breaking at an angle to the beach. Sometimes they will be caused by a combination of the two.

Lifesaving

Rip Tides

These are fast flowing runback currents which are very dangerous for swimmers in the sea. After the waves break onto the beach, the water flows out in the direction which causes the least resistance - this is the rip. To recognise a rip tide look for:

- discoloured water, brown in colour, due to sand stirred at the bottom
- foam on the surface which extends beyond the breaking waves
- a ripple appearance when the water around is generally calm (this is obviously more difficult to identify on a windy day or when the sea is choppy)
- debris floating with the current
- large waves breaking further out on both sides of the rip

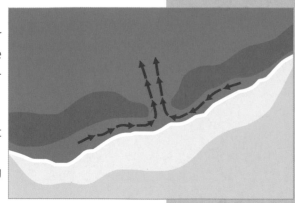

RIP TIDE

Survival in Rip Tides

- swim out of the rip by keeping parallel to the shore
- return to the shore through the breaking waves

Waves

Waves are caused by the wind. Their size and distance apart are determined by the distance over which the wind blows as well as the depth of the water.

Swimming in Waves

A swimmer or lifesaver must have the strength to break through a wave and gain as much distance as possible before the next wave. The best method is to:

- dive towards the bottom just before the wave arrives
- hold onto or pull along the bottom with both hands
- bring down your feet and place them on the bottom
- push off the bottom back to the surface on the seaward side of the wave
- swim until the next wave arrives and then repeat the action

4

*WARNING
Extreme care should
be taken when
swimming in waves,
particularly in
shallow water.*

SURVIVAL IN WAVES

Survival and Self-Rescue in Emergency Situations

Sometimes specialist survival knowledge may be required. Some of the most common situations in the UK demanding survival and self-rescue skills are listed below:

Underwater Weeds
- weeds will float apart if you move slowly, so avoid sudden movement
- sculling is probably the best technique as it makes breathing easy and reduces the amount of unnecessary movement
- alternatively swim very gently with a long, slow breast or side stroke with minimum leg movement

Weirs
- if drawn over a weir, attempt to get to the bottom by diving down, tuck your body into a ball and hold your breath until thrown to the surface

Quicksand and Deep Mud
- do not try to stand up
- spread your weight by lying flat on the surface, and move by slow arm and leg actions (it is often preferable to lie on your back)

Falling through Ice
- call for help
- spread your arms across the surface of the ice
- if it proves strong enough to support you, kick to a swimming position and slide onto the ice
- if the ice breaks, try to move towards safety breaking it as you go
- or wait for help by staying as still as possible to maintain body heat with arms spread across the ice

If someone else falls through ice
- send for help
- avoid going on to weakened ice
- try to reach the person with a pole or rope and pull to safety
- if you have to go across the ice to help - lie flat - move with caution - use a ladder - and spread your weight as evenly as possible over the ice

FALL THROUGH ICE

Lifesaving

Escape from a Car in Water

When a car enters the water, it may settle on the surface for a short time. Every attempt should be made to get out at this point through the side windows.

The car will sink engine first and contrary to a long held belief, there is not likely to be a significant air pocket when the car reaches the bottom.

A knowledge of the method of escaping will help the occupants to remain calm and make a plan. After the car hits the water, the following should be attempted in the order listed:

- unfasten your seatbelt
- switch on all interior and exterior lights so that the occupants can see and be seen
- make sure the doors are not locked
- only if unable to escape on the surface close all the windows, the tailgate or sunroof to maximise air pressure and prolong the car flotation time
- get into the back of a front engine car and try to open a back door or get into the front of a rear engine car and try to open a front door
- take a breath before the car finally submerges
- when the water reaches your chin, the pressure inside and outside the car will be equalised, take a deep breath and try to force the door open - if this fails, wind the window down and the door should open
- try to push out a windscreen or rear window with your feet if the doors or windows cannot be opened, placing the feet near a corner
- if there is more than one person in the car, link hands and go out in a human chain to make sure no one is left behind.
- if there is only one competent lifesaver in the car, that person should be last out
- occupants should tilt their heads backwards and whistle out air as they rise to the surface to reduce the pressure on the ears

4

REAR ENGINE CAR SINKING

FRONT ENGINE CAR SINKING

Survival Equipment

In addition to the items of equipment described above for use in specific emergency situations, it is helpful to have access to a range of survival equipment for use in different environments. The most commonly used items are listed below:

- personal flotation devices (PFDs)
- flares
- life buoys
- life boats
- survival clothing
- survival bags

- whistles
- life rings
- life rafts
- wet suits
- blankets
- ropes and harnesses

SAFETY AND SURVIVAL EQUIPMENT

4

Training and Assessing Survival & Self-Rescue

Check your understanding by answering the questions on survival and self-rescue below. Join a recognised lifesaving or lifeguard club to develop your knowledge and skills further.

Training

You should participate in a comprehensive survival and self-rescue programme that gives you the opportunity to practise personal as well as group survival skills. You will need to learn how to look after yourself and others in a variety of different environments. You should take part in staged survival and self-rescue incidents which will test your knowledge, skills, fitness and judgement.

Assessing

You should test your knowledge, understanding and ability in survival and self-rescue on a regular basis through RLSS UK trainer assessed survival and self-rescue awards or by attempting to gain one of the Society's major lifesaving or lifeguarding awards which contain externally assessed survival elements.

4

Checking your Understanding of Survival & Self-Rescue

The following questions are designed to check your knowledge and understanding of survival and self-rescue, as described in this chapter; alongside each question is the relevant page reference.

page 52	What are the five principles of a survival emergency plan?
page 54	What strategies should you use in a personal survival situation?
page 55	What are the four main distress signals?
page 56	When should you remove clothing in water?
page 57	What is the difference between a lifejacket and buoyancy jacket?
page 57	How should you enter water from a boat wearing a PFD?
page 58	What is hypothermia? How is it caused?
page 58	How would you know that someone was suffering from hypothermia?
page 59	What is the estimated survival time in water of 11°C?
page 60	What are the key principles for survival in cold water?
page 60	What do the letters H.E.L.P. stand for?
page 61	When would you use the HUDDLE position?
page 62	What are the two main types of sea current?
page 63	How would you recognise a rip tide?
page 63	How should you swim through waves?
page 64	What would you do if you got stuck in deep mud?
page 65	How would you escape from a sinking car?
page 66	What equipment might be useful in a survival situation?

Summary

Survival and self-rescue depend on good training and judgement. Practise your skills regularly on your own and with others, learn to expect the unexpected. Avoid dangerous areas and always advise others to do the same. While survival and self-rescue may require competent levels of fitness, skill and knowledge, the development of effective judgement will help you to ensure your own as well as other people's safety. Practise your skills in cold water under the supervision of a registered lifeguard club. Remember the biggest danger for most people, in a survival situation, is the cold.

4

COLD WATER SURVIVAL

Rescue Principles

Introduction to Rescue Principles

This chapter outlines the key principles and skills which could be employed in any emergency situation. On the following pages you will find information on:

- research into rescues
- steps in a rescue
- emergency action plan
- recognition of an emergency
- acceptance of responsibility
- assessing a situation
- planning a rescue
- performing a rescue
- providing aftercare
- evaluating and reporting a rescue

5

Research into Rescues

Over the past ten years, RLSS UK has played a prominent role in conducting research into the causes and effects of rescues. The first full report of its kind was published in 1988 and was based on a detailed analysis of over one thousand rescue reports of cases recorded by the Royal Humane Society (RHS).

The second part of the study, involving a three year examination of rescues recorded by the RHS, was started in 1993 . The key findings of that research are outlined below.

Location of Rescues

Most rescues are undertaken by untrained persons in inland locations. Many of these areas are not patrolled or supervised.

Time of Year

Inevitably, many rescues take place during the summer months when beaches, are full and the inexperienced open water user ventures too far into deep water or misjudges a situation. In the winter, as rivers flood and conditions become treacherous underfoot, a surprising number of rescues are successfully undertaken.

Time of Day

Lifesavers should be aware that emergency situations can occur at any time of the day or night. Indeed, it is likely that many rescues will take place after dark. Lifesavers must be prepared to act at any time and in any environment.

Age and Sex of Rescuers

On average, it takes at least two people to rescue one casualty. Rescuers are usually male and in their mid-teens to late thirties.

Lifesaving

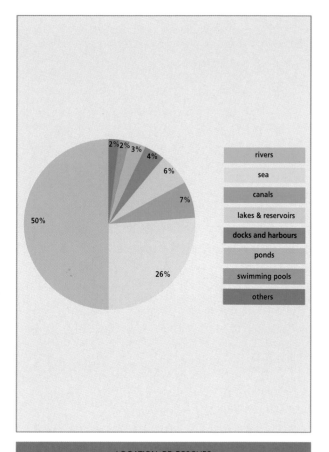

rivers

sea

canals

lakes & reservoirs

docks and harbours

ponds

swimming pools

others

2% 2% 3% 4% 6% 7% 50% 26%

LOCATION OF RESCUES

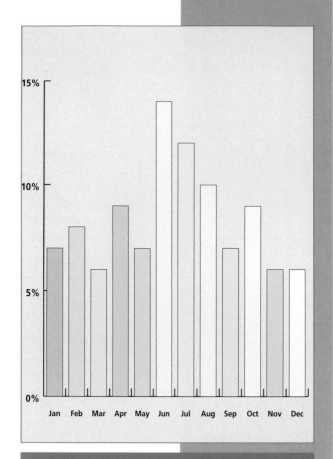

RESCUES BY TIME OF YEAR

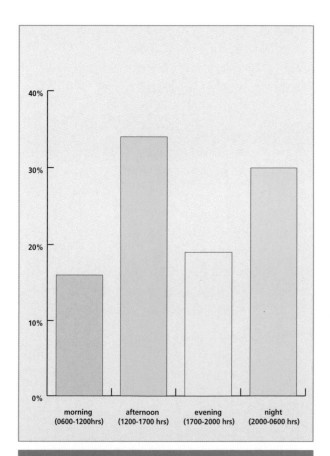

RESCUES BY TIME OF DAY

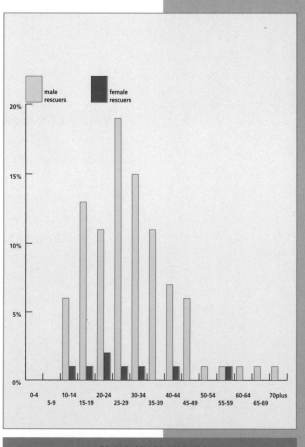

male rescuers

female rescuers

AGE AND SEX OF RESCUERS

Lifesaving

Age and Sex of Casualties

Most casualties are male and aged between the ages of five and fourteen years, emphasising the need for effective water safety training and education in schools and colleges.

Distance from Safety

The myth that a rescuer will have to swim miles out to sea to rescue a casualty has been dispelled by this and previous research. It is likely that, in many situations, the casualty may be less than 10 metres from land.

Rescue Aids

In over 60% of reported cases, rescue aids were not used by the rescuer, either because none were available or because the rescuer failed to take advantage of items which would have made effective rescue aids.

Specialist equipment is rarely available when needed, so often the rescuer is forced to improvise. The following items have all been used successfully as rescue aids:

belt	fishing line	pole
boat	fishing rod	raft
boat hook	inflatable dinghy	rake
box	inner tube	rescue ski
branch	jet ski	rope
cable	knife	safety harness
canoe	ladder	string
clothing	lifebelt	sailboard
corrugated iron	log	surfboard
crane	net	torch
diving equipment	plank	torpedo buoy

Reasons for Rescue

It is easy to imagine a dramatic rescue attempt in stormy seas, yet the reality is often quite different. A few of the many reasons for rescue are listed below:

- alcohol related
- crashed car
- cut off by tide
- caught in floods
- drugs related
- exhausted casualty

- fell in from boat
- fell from land
- fell through ice
- got cramp
- inflatable out of control
- injured casualty

5

Lifesaving

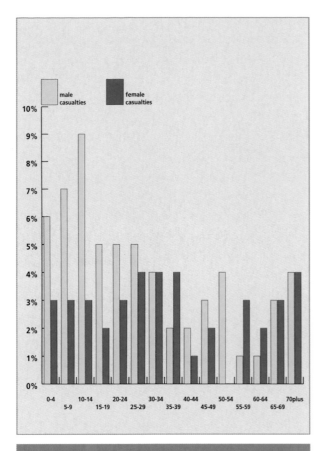

AGE AND SEX OF CASUALTIES

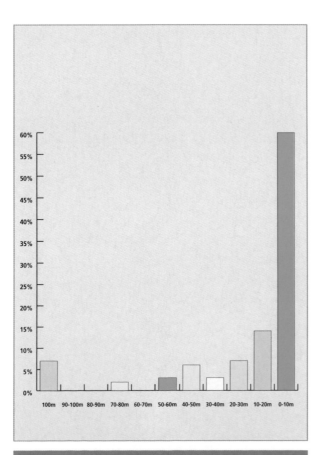

RESCUES BY DISTANCE FROM SAFETY

5

Many casualties get into difficulty as a result of the effects of alcohol and drug abuse, physical and mental disability. Indeed a casualty's condition may cause more problems than the weather, environment or distance from safety.

Evidence from this research emphasises the need to develop effective strategies and skills for dealing with any emergency situation. Whilst rescuing others may be physically and emotionally demanding, complex skills and equipment are rarely needed; however initiative is essential.

Using Initiative

All rescues demand the use of initiative and judgement. The best way to develop these essential skills is through training and discussion of how to deal with the unexpected.

The development of judgement should be the aim of all lifesavers. In most emergencies there will be choice of action open to the rescuer. If a rescue is to be effective and successful, you will need to be competent in the key areas of:

- **skill**
- **knowledge**
- **fitness**
- **judgement**

Look at the three scenarios opposite and decide how you would deal with each one in turn. Each of these emergency situations could be approached using a number of different strategies and skills. Emphasis should always be placed on safety.

Initiative Training

The purpose of initiative training is to develop judgement and decision making in applying known skills to unknown emergencies. The emphasis is very much on your ability to reason, to plan a course of action under pressure and to apply the most appropriate skills in situations where:

- conditions are as found by the rescuer
- entry points are designated
- careful selection of equipment and rescue aids is required
- casualties are realistic
- distances are variable
- priorities of rescue are tested

Training should be structured to give you the opportunity to apply the rescue sequence and develop the ability to prioritise correctly. Tests can range from the simple to the complex but should always challenge you!

5

Lifesaving

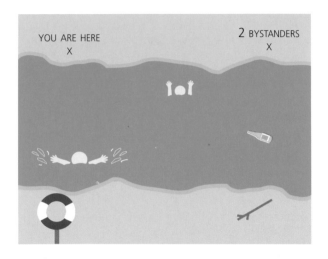

1 RESCUER, 2 CASUALTIES, 2 BYSTANDERS, 1 LIFE BUOY, 1 STICK AND 1 BOTTLE

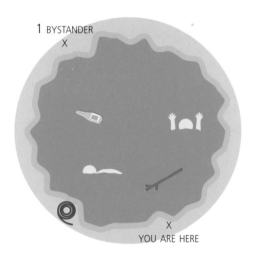

1 RESCUER, 2 CASUALTIES, 1 BYSTANDER, 1 ROPE, 1 BOTTLE AND 1 STICK

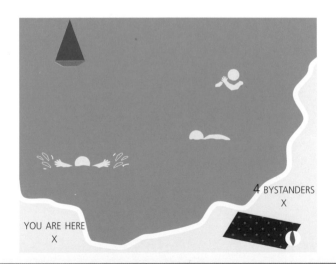

1 RESCUER, 3 CASUALTIES, 4 BYSTANDERS, 1 YACHT, 1 BEACH TOWEL AND 1 BEACH BALL

non swimmer

weak swimmer

unconscious casualty

injured casualty

5

*identify casualties
bystanders and
rescue aids*

↓

decide on priorities

↓

make action plan

↓

take action

↓

evaluate action

Rescue Principles

The key principles of rescue and the questions you need to ask yourself can be summarised as follows:

Alertness   **What is happening?**
- Recognising an Emergency   Is there an emergency?
- Accepting Responsibility   Can I or anyone else help?

Assessment   **What information have I got?**
- Assessing a Situation   What? Where? When? Who? How? Why?
- Making an Action Plan   What are the priorities? What shall I do?

Action   **Do it!**
- Performing a Rescue   Rescue sequence

Reassessment   **What has happened or changed?**
- Reviewing a Situation   What shall I do now?

Aftercare   **Who needs aftercare?**
- Providing Aftercare   What care is needed?

Evaluation   **How did it go?**
- Reviewing your Actions   What did I do? When? Where? Why?

Reporting   **Explaining what I did!**
- Providing Information   Write a report for the relevant authorities
                                       (as soon as possible after the incident)

Over the following pages, we will look at each of these areas in turn.

OPEN WATER RESCUE

Alertness

If you are to perform or assist in a rescue, there are two major factors which can influence the outcome:

- the ability to recognise a problem
- the ability to interpret the problem as an emergency requiring urgent action

Recognising an Emergency

How would you be able to recognise each of the following?

- someone has slipped on a river bank and fallen into the water
- a swimmer is making little or no headway in trying to return to the shore
- a child on an airbed has been caught in a current and is drifting out to sea
- a weak swimmer is chasing a ball into deep water

What would you expect to find if you saw or heard the following?

- a shout or a cry from deep water
- a group of people standing and watching
- an overturned boat
- someone rushing to the water's edge

Training in recognising problems and emergencies will help you to decide what action to take. Most importantly, you will need to be able to recognise the essential characteristics of drowning casualties.

5

Casualty Recognition

People in difficulty or who are drowning do not all display the same characteristics. Many people do not struggle or wave for help. Sometimes casualties have not been rescued because they were seen wearing lifejackets or swimming and were assumed to be in no immediate danger.

While drowning casualties may not always act in the same way, research has shown that there are essentially four categories of drowning casualties.

Casualty Simulation

Casualty simulation is invaluable in rescue training as it provides opportunities for varying the situation, creating realism and improving the recognition, assessment and judgement needed in an emergency. You should start practising casualty simulation and recognition from the earliest stages of any training programme.

For initiative tests to be effective, accurate simulation is essential. By acting the role of a drowning casualty you will learn to recognise and respond to the needs of a casualties in real life.

Categories of Drowning Casualty

There are four main categories of drowning casualty:

- **non-swimmer**
- **weak swimmer**
- **injured**
- **unconscious**

A fifth category, that of a competent swimmer in difficulty, may well fit into one or all of the above. The competent swimmer will take on different characteristics depending on the circumstances. The most likely conditions to turn a competent swimmer into a potential drowning casualty are:

- cold water
- alcohol
- rough water
- strong currents
- rip tides
- boating accidents
- environmental hazards
- spinal cord injury

Casualty with Spinal Cord Injury

Many rescuers are concerned about how to recognise a casualty suffering from spinal cord injury. The following are situations in which a spinal cord injury is possible:

- fall from a height
- casualty found unconscious for an unknown reason
- significant head injury
- diving or water slide injury

Physical signs which may indicate spinal injury are:

- pain at the position of injury
- loss of movement in the extremities or below the injury site
- loss of sensation or tingling in the extremities
- disorientation or unconsciousness
- back or neck deformity
- visible bruising over an area of the spinal column
- impaired breathing
- obvious head injury
- fluid or blood in the ears

Management of a spinal cord injury requires specialist training. Advice on how to handle a spinal injury casualty is contained in Chapter 6 (under Recovery Methods) and in the Society's Lifeguard Handbooks.

5

WARNING!
A drowning casualty rarely fits exactly the character descriptions that follow.
As conditions vary, so do people.

Lifesaving

NON-SWIMMER

WEAK SWIMMER

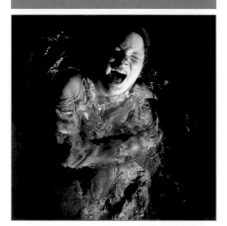

INJURED CASUALTY

UNCONSCIOUS CASUALTY

5

NON-SWIMMER

5

Non-Swimmer

Before Rescue

- may not be using arms and legs for support
- vertical and unsure of direction of help or land
- only concerned to maintain supply of air
- may submerge for increasing periods of time
- seldom waves or calls for help
- more intent on maintaining breathing
- wide eyed and panicked

During Rescue

- may not respond to instructions
- may attempt to grasp rescuer
- remains vertical in water
- may cease to panic when supported with head and shoulders clear of water

Implications for rescuer

- when unco-operative, only attempt a contact rescue if very experienced
- use a rescue aid (see chapter 6)

Weak Swimmer

Before Rescue

- could be using arms and legs for support
- at angle to surface, usually facing the side
- head may submerge periodically
- may be able to expel water entering mouth
- may wave and call for help
- varying degrees of anxiety in face and eyes

During Rescue

- may respond to clear instructions
- good when support is offered
- may be able to float on back and use some propulsive movements

Implications for rescuer

- accompanied and non-contact rescues are most suitable
- use a rescue aid (see chapter 6)

WEAK SWIMMER

Injured Casualty

Before Rescue

- may be in awkward position
- gripping injured part of body
- limited by nature of injury to attract attention
- calling out in pain
- facial expression shows varying degrees of pain and anxiety
- may be panicking and crying out in pain

During Rescue

- response to instruction poor - may be more concerned about injury
- maintains awkward position grasping site of injury
- may be in a state of panic

Implications for rescuer

- apply emergency care measures
- tow may be affected by awkward position in water
- avoid aggravating injury

INJURED CASUALTY

5

Unconscious Casualty

Before Rescue

- completely limp
- head may be only part of body visible
- may be floating at any point between surface and bottom, either face up or down
- no attempts to attract attention
- facial expression not usually seen during approach
- eyes probably closed

During Rescue

- no response to instructions
- no physical co-operation
- may be difficult to manoeuvre casualty

Implications for rescuer

- buoyancy may vary
- immediate contact and support needed
- contact tow necessary
- use buoyant aid, if available, for support
- expired air ventilation priority if not breathing (see chapter 7)
- cardiopulmonary resuscitation priority if no pulse (see chapter 7)

UNCONSCIOUS CASUALTY

Accepting Responsibility

People who witness an emergency are influenced by other spectators. For various reasons, some tend to avoid becoming involved.

Effects of Others

Each person present will make a personal judgement about the extent of the emergency and whether action is required. In making an assessment, you may notice that others are not reacting and therefore may not be of any assistance. If bystanders are untrained, their lack of reaction may be caused by not knowing what to do.

Effects of a Crowd

A crowd may affect your ability to act quickly. The more people that are present, the less responsibility each person may feel. This is rarely due to lack of care but more often to an over-reliance on others and an unwillingness to take the lead.

Implications for the Rescuer

Accepting responsibility for a situation and for your subsequent actions requires:

- ability to recognise an emergency situation (this will be improved through regular practice and coping with emergency situations in training)
- courage to overcome feelings of fear and nervousness provoked by dealing with the unknown
- willingness to take command of the situation and take responsibility for the rescue attempt
- ability to make decisions and take appropriate action
- ability to encourage and organise others in assisting and supporting a rescue attempt

Legal Responsibilities

As a bystander or witness to an emergency, you are not under any legal obligation to respond, particularly as conditions may be dangerous or you may lack the necessary experience or ability. However if you decide to accept responsibility for a rescue attempt, you could reasonably be expected to:

- provide a minimum standard of care when recovering, landing and treating the casualty
- act in good faith within the scope of your knowledge and training
- avoid causing further injury or giving care beyond your training
- look after the casualty until the emergency services or further assistance arrives
- respect the casualty's privacy and confidentiality, by ensuring that any information you receive or discover is discussed only with casualty and the emergency services
- provide a written record or report of the emergency including details of your actions, the casualties, the time and location of the situation (such information may be required by the police or a coroner's court in the unfortunate event of the casualty's death)

5

Assessment

Assessing a Situation

Whatever your ability and skills, after recognising an emergency and accepting responsibility, it is essential to spend time assessing the situation. Furthermore, it is important to try and make correct assessments, as misjudgments may cause difficulties later on and lead you into danger.

Think Before You Act

Assessment and consideration of the options should help you to develop a clear and effective plan of action. In aquatic facilities with supervising staff, this may well be within the guidelines of an existing NOP or EAP.

Ability of Rescuer

In the first instance, you will need to decide whether you have sufficient levels of knowledge, skill, fitness and judgement to perform a rescue. Competence in each of these areas means that you will be able to use:

- knowledge to understand information you gather about the environment, casualties and type of rescue required
- skill to perform the techniques required for a successful rescue
- fitness to perform the techniques required quickly, calmly and effectively
- judgement to apply your skills, knowledge and decisions wisely, whilst appreciating the level of fitness required to ensure your own safety

Factors Affecting Assessment

In addition to considering your own ability, a number of other factors may influence your assessment and hence your eventual plan of action:

- urgency required
- number and condition of casualties
- availability of rescue aids and assistance
- craft available
- distance from safety
- strength and direction of wind, tide or current
- hazards above, below or in water
- depth of water
- possible entry and exit points

Time Spent on Assessment

The actual time you spend assessing will vary depending on whether you are able to make an instant judgement (reaching out to grab someone) or whether you need to develop a full and deliberate plan which takes into account a wide range of factors (deciding how to rescue a group cut off by the tide on a cold and windy day). In some situations, it may only be necessary to inform someone in authority. If a personal rescue attempt is too dangerous, it may be best to shout, telephone or run for help.

WARNING!
No two emergency situations are the same! Actions will differ in every case.

5

WARNING!
Assessment time will vary depending on the situation. It is important to take time to make the right decision.

Your success in a rescue attempt will always be influenced by your ability to make calm, rational decisions.

Making an Action Plan

When making an action plan, you will need to consider the following factors:

- nature of area
- number of casualties
- priorities of rescue
- available assistance
- telephoning for help
- safety of rescuer
- rescue sequence
- personal capabilities
- leadership
- selection of rescue aids
- removal of clothing
- flexibility of action plan

We will now look at each of these factors in turn.

LAND BASED RESCUE

Nature of Area

Environmental conditions may affect your ability to:

- perform land based or wading rescues
- enter the water
- approach a casualty
- exit after rescue

Most rescues will be affected to some extent by waves, currents, steep or muddy banks, weeds or murky water.

Number of Casualties

The number and conditions of any casualties should be established immediately by:

- personal observation
- asking bystanders
- questioning casualties

If the number stated differs from those observed or rescued, an underwater search may be necessary.

Lifesaving

Priorities of Rescue

When more than one person is in difficulty, you will need to decide who to help first. Priority should normally be given to securing and supporting conscious casualties. Of these, the earliest priority should usually be for non-swimmers as they are in danger of submerging.

Nevertheless, it may be possible to provide early support to others quickly and easily without significantly delaying the rescue of any non-swimmers. Attention can then be given to unconscious or submerged casualties.

Time is a critical factor when determining priorities in a rescue. If a casualty is conscious but in danger of submerging, it may be only a matter of minutes before irreversible brain damage occurs, due to lack of oxygen. If a casualty is unconscious, unless you saw the casualty's condition change, brain damage may already have occurred.

It is likely that once a casualty stops breathing, the heart will stop. Within 4-6 minutes brain damage is possible and after 10 minutes irreversible brain damage is probable.

- **security of conscious non-swimmer**
- **security of conscious injured or weak swimmer**
- **security of unconscious casualty**

The precise order of rescue will be determined by the nature of the emergency, the number, type and position of casualties, the rescue aids and assistance available, the environmental conditions, the distance of the casualties from safety and, of course, your own rescuing capabilities. In general terms, the main priorities of rescue can best be summarised as follows:

- telephone or send for help
- ensure safety of rescuer
- ensure safety of those in danger
- recover casualties from water
- provide aftercare & support

Available Assistance

In most cases, before you start a rescue attempt, you should go and get or send someone to ask for further assistance as this will increase the likelihood of the rescue being successful. Only in situations where the rescue can be completed quickly and safely or where help may come too late should you attempt the rescue without further assistance.

Bystanders may be able to help you by being sent to call for an ambulance or the police or by being sent to find and bring back rescue aids. They may also be able to assist with the rescue itself by providing essential liformation about the situation or by helping to land a casualty.

RESCUE PRIORITIES

Help

↓

Safety

↓

Conscious

Casualties

↓

Unconscious

Casualties

↓

Aftercare

5

REMEMBER!
Act calmly but decisively. Give clear, firm instructions and make certain they are understood.

DIAL "999"

TELEPHONING FOR HELP

Telephoning for Help

When sending someone to telephone for help, instruct the person to dial 999 and ask for one of the following services:

- **fire**
- **ambulance**
- **cave rescue**
- **police**
- **mountain rescue**
- **coastguard**

The operator of the emergency service will ask them for the following information:

- telephone number shown on the phone
- place where help is needed
- what has happened
- number of people involved
- condition of casualties
- name, home address and telephone number of person phoning

Instruct them to return to the scene to help or stay by the phone to help direct the emergency services to the scene.

Safety of Rescuer

Your safety as a rescuer is the most important consideration. Too many people drown or get into difficulty attempting rescues that are beyond their own capabilities.

Rescues that can be performed without entering the water are the safest (for example, a land based reach or throw rescue), followed by wading rescues or attempts making use of boats or other water craft (where you have appropriate experience). Only if none of these are suitable should you consider using a swimming rescue.

Rescue Sequence

Rescues should be undertaken, where possible, in the following order: shout, signal, reach, throw, wade, row, swim with an aid, swim and tow. If you follow this sequence you should be able to look after your own safety and rescue a number of casualties.

Personal Capabilities

Decide whether you can perform a rescue quickly and effectively using appropriate techniques. If the situation requires a swimming rescue, you will need to be certain that you have sufficient fitness, knowledge and skill to perform all aspects of the rescue on your own or whether you will need to enlist the help and support of others.

5

RESCUE SEQUENCE

shout

↓

signal

↓

reach

↓

throw

↓

wade

↓

row

↓

swim with an aid

↓

swim and tow

Selection of Rescue Aids

Look around carefully for possible rescue aids, before making your selection. Your final choice of one or more rescue aids will be influenced by the following criteria:

- **availability** - easily accessible or rapidly improvised
- **portability** - easily carried to the scene and, if necessary, towed through the water
- **rigidity** - stable and able to allow a casualty to lean against it
- **size** - large enough to prevent direct contact with the casualty
- **shape** - suitable for rescue method selected
- **buoyancy** - capable of supporting and giving confidence to casualty
- **safety** - easily and safely used by rescuer and casualty

Useful Rescue Equipment

The following items of equipment have proved to be the most useful in rescue situations. Some are produced especially for rescue purposes, others are more everyday items found near water locations or carried by water users:

- **torpedo buoy** - regularly used by lifeguards, has sufficient buoyancy for two people, a long cord and a harness to allow a safe distance between casualty and rescuer
- **rubber ring, life buoy, large drinks container** - good buoyancy and rigidity, very common, prevents contact with rescuer and, depending on size, provides adequate to excellent support for casualty
- **rope, line, throwbag** - often available as public rescue equipment, regularly used by lifeguards, no buoyancy or rigidity, keeps distance between rescuer and casualty
- **branch, stick, fishing rod, paddle** - rigid though not providing much support, keeps distance between rescuer and casualty, very common in water areas
- **inflatable bed, surf board or ski** - good buoyancy, varying degrees of rigidity, supports casualty or allows distance to be kept between casualty and rescuer
- **clothing or towel** - keeps distance between rescuer and casualty, very common though non-buoyant

Practise with different rescue aids, in different environments. In any rescue, any form of rescue aid is better than none.

RESCUE AIDS

5

Action

Leadership

When other people are available to help, make certain you have only one person who is designated to lead the rescue attempt. This should ensure that people and resources are used quickly and effectively. As leader you should:

- take the initiative
- ask searching questions of bystanders
- provide clear and precise instructions
- allocate responsibilities to each rescuer
- follow an action plan
- maintain control of the situation to the end
- ensure the safety of all in the area

Removal of Clothing

The time involved in removing clothing must be balanced against the time required to reach the casualty as well as the environmental conditions to be encountered. Remember:

- shoes may prevent feet from being cut in rocky areas
- lightweight summer clothing does not seriously impede swimming
- heavy clothing will drag and increase tiredness (leave it on land)
- layers of clothing will help to retain body heat in cold water
- items of clothing may be useful rescue aids
- some dry clothing may be needed after the rescue

Rescue

Once you have decided on your action plan, act quickly and decisively. When help is available, you should continue to act while others go for help or rescue other casualties. Full details of the essential rescue skills are described in the next chapter.

Flexibility of Action

Conditions may change a number of times during a rescue (a throwing aid may miss the casualty, a non-swimmer may become unconscious or the weather may change). Keep reviewing your action plan. Remember that in any rescue, flexibility is the key to success and safety. Keep within your own capabilities and review your decisions regularly.

5

RESCUE

Reassessment

Reviewing a Situation

During the course of the rescue, you may need to review and revise your action plan. You may have to do this because one or more of the following circumstances may have changed:

- weather or environmental conditions
- number or condition of the casualties
- distance to be covered
- suitability of rescue aids
- suitability of rescue techniques
- suitability of landing or exit point

In such circumstances, it is essential to:

- take time to observe the situation again
- review how the conditions have changed
- consider what you have achieved so far
- decide whether it is safe to continue
- consider what action to take next

SECURING A CASUALTY

When you have made your decision and readjusted your action plan, continue to act quickly, calmly and effectively until the rescue is complete.

5

Aftercare

Providing Aftercare & Support

At the end of the rescue, you will need to decide which casualties require immediate aftercare and, more particularly, what type of aftercare is needed. Such care and support will vary depending on the number and condition of casualties, environmental factors, assistance available and your own knowledge of life support and first aid. Your priorities are:

- cardiopulmonary resuscitation (CPR)
- management of choking
- control of bleeding
- care of the unconscious, breathing casualty
- treatment for shock
- medical assistance

Further information on aftercare and support is provided in Chapter 7.

AFTERCARE

Evaluation

Reviewing a Rescue Attempt

It is important to spend time on your own or with someone else discussing and reviewing the rescue attempt. This will be particularly helpful to you if the rescue attempt was unsuccessful.

In a training environment, talking through what you saw and did will enable others to comment more constructively on the rescue attempt and provide you with positive feedback. When reviewing a rescue attempt, you should ask yourself these questions:

- what did I see?
- what was my assessment of the situation?
- what were my priorities?
- what was my plan?
- what assistance did I use?
- what rescue aids did I use?
- what action did I take?
- why did I take that action?
- how did I reassess the situation?
- how did the rescue attempt end?
- how could I have improved my plans and action?
- how do I feel now?

5

Reporting

Informing the Authorities

Many people who are involved in emergency situations whether as rescuers, casualties or bystanders often want to avoid publicity and attention. However, as a rescuer you should make certain that the relevant authorities are informed of what happened, preferably in writing.

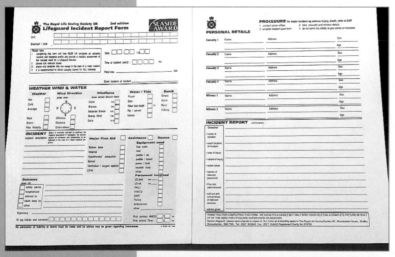

Sometimes this will be taken out of your hands by the police or emergency services, on other occasions you may need to contact a local authority office or the owner of a stretch of water, particularly where the emergency situation was caused by dangerous environmental conditions or where the public rescue equipment was damaged.

In addition to informing these bodies, the Royal Life Saving Society UK is always anxious to receive reports of rescue attempts, as part of its programme of research into the causes and outcomes of aquatic emergency situations.

RESCUE REPORT FORM

Writing a Rescue Report

The following information will usually be needed, if you are asked to provide a report of a rescue:

- your name, address and signature
- names, addresses, ages and sex of rescuers
- names, addresses, ages and sex of casualties
- names and addresses of any witnesses
- location of emergency situation
- day, month and year of rescue
- time of the rescue
- description of what happened
- distance of casualties from land
- distance covered by rescuers
- details of any rescue aids used
- details of any aftercare given
- details of medical assistance provided
- outcome of the rescue
- authorities contacted
- any other information you consider relevant
- map or line drawing of situation

RESCUE CERTIFICATE

The Royal Humane Society (address at the back of this book) presents gallantry awards to members of the public. Nominations are usually made by the Police Chief Constable of the area in which the rescue took place. The Royal Life Saving Society UK makes a number of annual awards for rescues including Certificates of Commendation and Meritorious Action. The Mountbatten Medal is awarded to a member of the public who is judged by the Commonwealth Council to have performed the most proficient and exceptional rescue during a year. Nominations for this award should be made in writing to the Director General as soon as possible after the rescue has taken place.

Training and Assessing Rescue Principles

Check your knowledge and understanding of rescue principles. You should join a recognised lifesaving or lifeguard club to practise and develop your ability and skills in this area.

Training

You should learn through practise and experience how to apply the rescue principles described in this chapter to a variety of different situations and environments. A major part of your training and learning should involve the use of initiative. While fitness, knowledge and skill are important, the development of judgement is probably the most important aspect of becoming a competent lifesaver.

Assessing

You should test your knowledge, understanding and application of rescue principles on a regular basis, through class based initiative and incident training and by gaining RLSS UK trainer assessed or externally assessed lifesaving awards.

Checking your Understanding of Rescue Principles

The following questions are designed to check your knowledge and understanding of rescue principles, as described in this chapter. Alongside each question is the relevant page reference.

page 70	What is the most recorded time during the day for a rescue?
page 72	What reasons are given for rescues being necessary?
page 74	What are the four main elements of initiative training?
page 76	What are the key principles of a rescue?
page 78	What are the four main categories of drowning casualty?
page 78	How might you recognise a spinal injury casualty?
page 82	What are the main responsibilities of a rescuer to a casualty?
page 83	How would you assess a situation? What factors would you consider?
page 85	What are the main priorities of rescue?
page 86	How would you instruct someone to telephone for help?
page 86	What is the usual sequence for a rescue?
page 87	What are the most useful buoyant rescue aids?
page 89	What factors would you consider when reassessing a situation?
page 89	What are the main priorities of aftercare?
page 90	Why is it important to evaluate a rescue attempt?
page 91	Who should you inform after completing a rescue? Why?

5

Summary

All successful rescues are based on the principles and guidelines outlined in this chapter. They are logical, easy to remember and when applied in sequence will help you to assess, plan and act carefully and decisively. Remember that a competent rescuer needs to develop effective levels of knowledge, fitness, skill and, most of all, judgement.

NEWS HEADLINES

Rescue Skills

6

Introduction to Rescue Skills

This chapter provides information on when and how the essential skills of rescue. On the following pages you will find information about:

- rescue methods
- towing methods
- defensive methods
- escape methods
- recovery methods
- support methods
- resuscitation in water
- casualty landings

All these skills are linked to the rescue sequence chart illustrated below:

SHOUT

SIGNAL

REACH

THROW

WADE

ROW

SWIM WITH AN AID

SWIM AND TOW

RESCUE SEQUENCE CHART

6

Shout and Signal Rescue

This is the safest form of rescue as it relies on the use of voice and hand signals and avoids contact with the casualty in the water.

You should use a shout and signal rescue when a casualty is conscious, close to the side and able to respond to instructions; where no rescue aids are available reassurance is necessary and you need to perform other rescue skills.

- attract the attention of the casualty by shouting and signalling
- give clear instructions to the casualty
- using hand signals and your voice, instruct the casualty to the side
- instruct and assist the casualty to a position of safety

SHOUT AND SIGNAL RESCUE

6

RIGID AID RESCUE

NON RIGID AID RESCUE

Reach Rescue

This is a highly effective and safe method of rescue, as the rescuer remains on land throughout. You should use a reach rescue when a land based rescue is possible, the casualty is close to the side and suitable rescue aids are available.

With a rescue aid

- select an available rescue aid
- attract the casualty's attention by shouting & signalling
- lie down on your front keeping the casualty under observation
- anchor yourself firmly, either using an assistant or by grasping a fixed object
- reach out with your rescue aid and instruct the casualty to take hold of it
- using a rigid aid - hold it just to the side of the casualty (if the aid is not grasped, hook it under the casualty's arm pit to provide support)
- using a non-rigid aid - keep hold of one end and throw the other end towards the casualty, where more distance is needed two items of clothing can be tied together (wet clothing is better than dry)
- if the aid is not grasped, put it in direct contact with the casualty if this is unsuccessful, alternative rescue methods will need to be considered
- pull the casualty steadily to safety
- if you are in danger of being pulled in, let go and try again when you are more secure
- instruct the casualty to a position of safety

Without a rescue aid

- attract the casualty's attention by shouting & signalling
- lie down or find a secure position, keeping the casualty under observation
- anchor yourself firmly, either using an assistant or by grasping a fixed object
- reach out with your hand and grasp the outside of the casualty's wrist
- pull the casualty steadily to safety
- if you are in danger of being pulled in, let go and try again when you are more secure
- instruct or assist the casualty to a position of safety

WITHOUT A RESCUE AID

Throw Rescue

This rescue can be used over a considerable distance, avoids direct contact with the casualty and makes use of a number of different rescue aids. The rescuer remains on land throughout. You should use a throw rescue when a land based rescue is possible, the distance or rescue aid is unsuitable for a reach rescue and a casualty needs help quickly.

BUOYANT AID THROW

With a buoyant aid
- choose an available aid, for example a rubber ring or plastic container (a ball is unsuitable in most cases)
- attract the casualty's attention by shouting and signalling
- indicate that you are about to throw something and show the casualty how to use it
- stand back from the edge and throw the aid roundarm, overarm or underarm, depending on the type of aid, the distance to the casualty and your standing position
- attempt to place the aid within reach and in front of the casualty, remembering to take into account the direction of the wind, tide or current and the weight of the aid
- instruct the casualty to hold the aid securely and kick to the side
- assist the casualty out of the water, taking care not to be pulled in
- if the casualty does not respond or if the aid fails to reach the casualty, use another aid or alternative rescue methods

UNWEIGHTED ROPE THROW

With a rope
- select a suitable length of rope, attract the casualty's attention and indicate that a rope is about to be thrown
- stand away from the edge in a safe position, coil the rope evenly
- before throwing, secure one end of the rope (either by tying it to a fixed object, knotting one end and placing it under foot or by holding the end of the rope in your hand)
- throw the rope to the casualty, allowing for wind or current
- if the rope lands out of reach, recoil the rope and throw again
- instruct the casualty to grasp the rope with both hands and face you
- haul in steadily, using a hand over hand method , observing the casualty all the way
- let go if you are in danger of being pulled in
- instruct or assist the casualty out of the water

There are several methods for coiling and throwing a rope. Make certain that you practise regularly. Practice makes perfect!

6

WEIGHTED ROPE THROW

Wade Rescue

This water based rescue requires careful entry into shallow water and brings the rescuer close to the casualty. It may enable a reach or throw rescue to be attempted.

You should use a wade rescue when the water is shallow and casualty is too far away for a land based rescue; when attempts to reach and throw from land have been unsuccessful and when the current and water conditions permit a safe entry.

With a rigid, buoyant or non-buoyant aid

- find a suitable reaching or throwing aid
- calm and reassure the casualty
- enter shallow water safely after using rescue aid to test depth (where possible)
- wade by sliding your feet carefully along the bottom, testing the depth with your rescue aid
- ensure the bottom is firm and free from obstructions before transferring your weight onto your front foot
- reach or throw the aid to the casualty giving clear instructions on how to hold it
- when a buoyant aid is used, throw it just in front of the casualty (as described earlier)
- when the aid has been grasped, encourage the casualty to return to safety
- avoid direct contact with the casualty until you reach the side
- let go, if you are in danger of being grabbed
- assist the casualty to land and provide aftercare

WADE RESCUE

Row Rescue

This rescue is suitable for use over a wide range of distances, if you are familiar with the craft. The word "row" is used as a generic term for all types of boats and rescue craft and includes:

- **sailing craft** - (yacht, dinghy, sailboard)
- **steering craft** - (jet ski, power boat)
- **paddle craft** - (rescue board, surf ski, canoe, rowing boat)

ROWING

You should only use a row rescue when you or someone else present is a competent and experienced user of the craft; a boat or rescue craft is available; or when shout, signal, reach, throw and wade rescues are not possible due to depth of water or distance involved.

Using a small craft

- choose the most suitable craft and aids available for your skills and experience
- board the craft carefully, wearing a PFD
- proceed directly to the casualty allowing for wind and currents
- decide where is the best point to make contact with the casualty (this will usually mean the boat being on the downwind and downstream side to prevent it drifting over the casualty)
- if you are using a power craft, always approach the casualty from downwind and downstream, turn off the engine when your are about three boat lengths away from the casualty, drift or paddle to the casualty, bring the casualty on board before restarting the engine
- use low risk rescue methods (talk, reach, throw) where possible
- encourage and reassure the casualty by giving clear instructions
- throw a buoyant aid to the casualty for support
- continue to calm and reassure the casualty before instructing the casualty to move to the stern of the boat (unless a power boat is being used when the casualty should be helped aboard over the side of the craft)
- if the casualty is unconscious and not breathing, you can give expired air ventilation in the water by leaning over the side of the boat
- tow or transport the casualty to safety (if injured or unconscious, another rescuer will be needed)
- assist the casualty to land and provide aftercare

CANOE

SURF SKI

DINGHY

POWERBOAT

PRE ENTRY

Swim Rescue

This method of rescue should only be used when shout, signal, reach, throw, wade and row rescues are unsuccessful or inappropriate for the situation. You must assess the situation carefully, make a clear plan and be aware of your own limitations as a rescuer. You will need to have a thorough understanding of the rescue principles outlined in the previous chapter.

- land based, wade and row rescues are unsuitable or have proved unsuccessful
- a casualty is away from the side or unconscious

Pre-Entry

- select a suitable buoyant or non-buoyant rescue aid (buoyant aids are best but not always available)
- carry the aid safely and efficiently so that your range of movement is not affected (buoyant aids should be held in front of the body or towed by using an attached line, while non-buoyant aids, such as clothing, should be tucked into your swimming costume or tied around your waist)
- remove any unnecessary clothing
- decide on your method of entry after considering:
    - depth and clarity of water
    - height of entry
    - type of rescue aid being carried
    - degree of urgency (depending on condition of casualty)

ENTRY

Entry

Enter the water carefully, by selecting the most appropriate method of entry for the conditions, from the following list (these skills are described in the swimming section).

- **slide in** - safest entry for low and steep sides, where conditions are unknown or care is needed
- **wade in** - water is shallow, murky and condition of bottom is unknown
- **compact jump** - water is deep, side of bank is high and steep
- **straddle entry** - water is deep, conditions are known, side is less than one metre high
- **shallow dive** - water is clear, bottom is free from obstacles, depth is at least 1.5 metres

Keep the casualty under observation, where possible, before, during and after the entry.

Lifesaving

Initial Approach

- wade through shallow water or swim after entry into deep water
- approach using front crawl or breast stroke
- swim out to the casualty, maintaining balance between speed and conservation of energy
- observe the casualty regularly throughout the approach swim, giving regular instructions, encouragement and reassurance

Final Approach

- swim slowly, cautiously and with your head out of the water as you approach the casualty (breast stroke is best as it provides good observation)
- move into the defensive stand-off position (described later in this section) at least **three metres** away from the casualty, make your final assessment and issue further instructions
- if you need to move behind the casualty, swim slowly in a wide circle, keeping the casualty in sight and instructing the casualty to keep looking forwards
- never swim underwater behind a casualty or lunge forward as this may cause panic
- when approaching an unconscious casualty, speed is essential and continuous observation will be needed in case the casualty submerges

The following pages describe when and how to use different methods of swimming rescue.

INITIAL APPROACH

6

FINAL APPROACH

PASSING A BUOYANT AID

Swim with an Aid Rescue

This method of rescue is used when a casualty is conscious and co-operative and may be able to assist the rescuer or when direct contact would be dangerous. There are two main types of swim with an aid rescues:

- **accompanied rescue**
- **non-contact rescue**

Always attempt an accompanied rescue first as it is a safer rescue method. If it is unsuccessful and further help is not available, attempt a non-contact tow using a suitable towing aid.

Accompanied Rescue

You should use an accompanied rescue when a casualty is too far from safety to be rescued by a reach, throw or wade rescue; no craft is available; the casualty is a weak or injured swimmer.

- select a suitable buoyant aid
- enter the water in a manner appropriate for the conditions
- approach and reassure the casualty
- adopt a defensive stand-off position (about three metres away from the casualty)
- instruct the casualty to grasp the rescue aid when it is thrown or passed
- float the aid or throw the aid carefully in front of the casualty
- assure the casualty that the aid will provide sufficient support
- instruct the casualty to kick while holding the aid
- accompany the casualty to safety, observing the direction of travel and the casualty throughout
- assist to land and provide aftercare

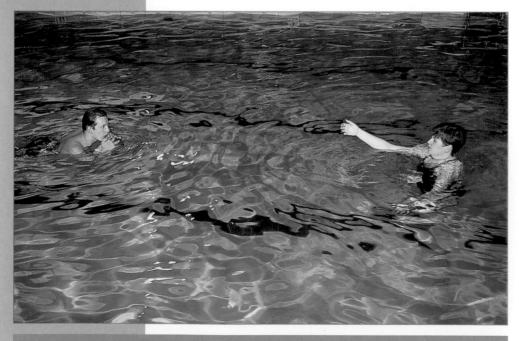

ACCOMPANIED RESCUE

Non-Contact Rescue

You should use a non contact rescue when an accompanied rescue has proved unsuccessful or impossible; where no boat is available; the casualty is a weak, injured or non-swimmer.

- select a suitable towing aid
- enter the water carefully using a method appropriate for the conditions
- approach the casualty
- adopt a defensive stand-off position and explain clearly what you are going to do
- pass one end of the aid to the casualty, keeping hold of the other end
- instruct the casualty to hold onto the aid with both hands and either stretch forwards with head up or turn and hold one end close to the chest (this second method makes it easier for you to tow as it creates less resistance, however in many situations the casualty or may be afraid to turn round)
- tow the casualty, by keeping your towing arm straight to avoid jerky movements which may send water over the casualty's face
- use side stroke or lifesaving back stroke
- watch where you are going
- observe the casualty regularly, looking out for signs of panic
- give plenty of reassurance and encourage the casualty to assist by kicking
- on reaching the side, assist to land and provide aftercare

NON CONTACT RESCUE - CASUALTY ON FRONT

If the casualty attempts to grasp you

- let go of the aid
- reverse away
- adopt the defensive stand-off position
- calm and reassure the casualty
- resume the tow only when it is safe to do so

NON CONTACT RESCUE - CASUALTY ON BACK

Swim and Tow Rescue

This rescue method requires a contact tow. It is the most difficult, dangerous and demanding form of rescue and should only be used as a last resort. It should only ever be attempted by an experienced and competent rescuer.

Risk of Contact

Any person who is in difficulty and close to drowning may be in a high state of panic and struggling violently. Often this will mean that the casualty's strength appears to outstrip that of the rescuer. Risk is increased by a drowning casualty:

- seizing upon any nearby object in an attempt to keep above water
- gaining additional strength or suffering from extreme fear
- refusing to release the rescuer from a sudden clutch
- thrashing their limbs and making progress through the water more difficult

Key Principles

To be effective a tow must: ·

- keep the casualty's mouth and face above the surface at all times
- give you control over the casualty
- enable you and the casualty to lie almost horizontally in the water (reducing resistance)
- allow you freedom of movement when swimming
- provide maximum safety, especially when towing a conscious casualty
- enable observation of the casualty and the direction of travel
- demand only reasonable amounts of stamina and energy for the conditions
- enable quick releases and escapes if the casualty struggles

6

SWIM AND TOW RESCUE

Using a Contact Tow

You should use a contact tow only when the full rescue sequence has proved unsuccessful or unsuitable; the casualty is unconscious; no aids are available; the casualty refuses to grasp a rescue aid.

SWIM AND TOW RESCUE

- always take a rescue aid with you (a buoyant aid may be useful in providing extra support for the casualty or yourself as the conditions change)
- swim cautiously towards the casualty
- calm and reassure the casualty
- adopt the defensive stand-off position at least three metres away from the casualty
- assess the condition of the casualty and select a suitable tow (see descriptions of tows)
- choose a tow which suits your ability, the casualty's condition, the environmental conditions and that will be effective over the distance of the return swim
- explain to the casualty what you are going to do
- swim slowly round the casualty in a wide arc, maintaining a safe distance until you are ready to move in behind the casualty and begin the tow
- tow the casualty calmly through the water, giving regular reassurance (change the tow if you or the casualty are becoming tired or uncomfortable)
- encourage the casualty to assist you by kicking or sculling
- keep observing the casualty and the direction of travel

If the casualty struggles or tries to grasp you
- let go of the casualty immediately
- reverse away
- adopt a defensive position stand-off
- calm and reassure the casualty
- move slowly around and behind the casualty
- resume the tow when it is safe, using a tow appropriate for an unco-operative casualty

If the casualty continues to struggle or tries to grasp you again
- let go of the casualty
- reverse away
- adopt a defensive stand-off position
- calm and reassure the casualty
- use a different tow appropriate for an unco-operative casualty
- support the casualty until help arrives

If the casualty is unconscious
- select a tow which gives you control of the casualty's head position and enables you to keep the airway open and prevent water washing over the face

6

Towing Methods

Practise using a variety of towing methods. You need to be able to select and adapt each method to suit the situation and to ensure that the tow is effective. You should be familiar with the methods listed and described below:

- **extended tow**
- **wrist tow**
- **cross chest tow**
- **head tow**
- **clothing tow**
- **chin tow**
- **shoulder tow**
- **support tow**

Extended Tow

You can use an extended tow when a casualty is passive or co-operative and conditions are calm.

- take hold of the casualty's chin or hair
- use a strong and effective kick
- encourage the casualty to assist by kicking and sculling
- keep your arm straight (elbow locked) and in line with the casualty
- keep observing the casualty and the direction of travel

EXTENDED TOW

Clothing Tow

You can use a clothing tow when a casualty is clothed, passive, co-operative and conditions are calm.

- grasp the clothing behind the casualty's neck
- grip as much material as possible below the collar to avoid choking the casualty
- relax your towing arm so that the casualty is lying directly in line with your shoulders
- keep your towing arm slightly bent to absorb any jerking movements
- instruct the casualty to assist by kicking or sculling
- keep observing the casualty and the direction of travel

6

CLOTHING TOW

Lifesaving

Wrist Tow

You can use a wrist tow when a casualty is co-operative and conditions are calm.

- grasp the back of the casualty's wrist
- hold the casualty's arm straight with your arm slightly bent at the elbow
- swim side stroke, where possible
- encourage the casualty to assist by kicking and sculling with their free hand
- keep observing the casualty and the direction of travel

Chin Tow

You can use a chin tow when conditions are rough and you need to maintain firm control of the casualty.

- place one hand on the casualty's chin
- move behind the casualty's head
- rest the casualty's head on your shoulder (on the same side as your towing arm)
- place the elbow of your towing arm against the casualty's shoulder
- swim using an effective kick (lifesaving backstroke is best)
- maintain close contact throughout the tow (cheek to cheek with casualty)
- keep observing the casualty and the direction of travel

WRIST TOW

CHIN TOW

6

CROSS CHEST TOW

Cross Chest Tow

You can use a cross chest tow when water conditions are rough and a casualty is unconscious or needs close control.

- approach the casualty from behind
- pass one arm over the corresponding shoulder and chest of the casualty with the elbow at right angles
- grip under the armpit and clamp the elbow to the casualty's chest
- use side stroke, where possible
- keep observing the casualty and the direction of travel

Shoulder Tow

You can use a shoulder tow when water conditions are rough, a casualty is unconscious or you need to maintain head elevation and control of the casualty.

- approach the casualty from behind
- hook one or both hands under the casualty's armpit(s) and grasp the shoulder(s)
- with the casualty firmly held, use an effective kick to tow the casualty to shore
- tighten or loosen the hold to maintain greater or lesser control over the casualty
- keep observing the casualty and the direction of travel

DOUBLE SHOULDER TOW

6

Lifesaving

Head Tow

You can use a head tow when a firm hold of the casualty's head is required.

- approach the casualty from behind
- place your hands firmly on the side of the casualty's head, with your palms facing inwards, fingers facing upwards and thumbs facing towards you
- avoid covering the casualty's ears and throat
- use any effective kick
- keep observing the casualty and the direction of travel

Support Tow

You can use a support tow when a casualty's head needs supporting; a casualty is unconscious; a buoyant aid is available; expired air ventilation in water is required (see section on resuscitation in the water).

- approach the casualty from behind
- position the buoyant aid under the casualty's shoulder (you can also hold it in place by hand)
- use any effective kick
- keep observing the casualty and the direction of travel

HEAD TOW

SUPPORT TOW

6

MULTIPLE RESCUE

WARNING!

Rescuing two or more casualties at the same time is both dangerous and exhausting. Your safety must always come first. Be aware of your own capabilities. Always follow the rescue sequence.

Multiple Rescue

This rescue method should only be attempted by strong and experienced rescuers in situations where two or more casualties need rescuing from the same situation or where two or more casualties are grouped together and it is impossible to separate them.

You should attempt a multiple rescue only when two or more casualties are in the same situation or grouped together; no assistance is available; you have the experience and ability to cope with the situation.

From Land or Water

- carefully observe and assess the situation
- make an action plan following the rescue principles outlined earlier
- make use of other rescuers and bystanders
- review and adjust your action plan as necessary
- avoid entering the water unless you have no other alternative
- follow the rescue sequence
- look after your own safety at all times
- make use of every available rescue aid

Buoyant aids can be used to provide support for one casualty, while you tow another to safety or to support more than one casualty if the aid has sufficient buoyancy.

Buoyant and non-buoyant aids can be used to separate two or more casualties without making direct physical contact or to tow two casualties to safety.

Towing Two Casualties

You should only tow two casualties to safety at the same time when both casualties are completely calm and you have enough physical strength.

- position the casualties on their backs, side by side
- swim behind and between them
- use a non-contact or, if necessary, a contact tow
- instruct the casualties to assist by kicking and sculling
- keep observing the casualties and the direction of travel

DOUBLE TOW

Lifesaving

Separating Two Casualties Locked Together

You should only attempt to separate two casualties locked together when the two casualties can not be towed together; one casualty has grasped another swimmer for support; you are an experienced and competent lifesaver; you have sufficient physical strength. Before doing anything, calm and reassure both casualties. Then use one of the following rescues:

Buoyant Aid Rescue

- select a buoyant aid and place it between the two casualties
- instruct one or both of the casualties to grasp hold of it
- tow or instruct them back to safety

Contact Rescue Method 1

- wait and exercise good judgement
- act speedily to separate both casualties when they are about to submerge
- grasp the uppermost casualty under the armpits from behind
- force both casualties down underwater
- place both legs around the first casualty and against the hips and thighs of the second casualty
- maintaining your grip on the first casualty's body, straighten your legs and force the two casualties apart
- if a buoyant aid is available, give it to the stronger casualty for support, while you tow the other casualty to safety

Contact Rescue Method 2

- approach from behind the uppermost or heavier casualty
- lock both hands and arms under the casualty's armpits and shoulders
- tow both casualties into shallow water and assist them to stand up
- be prepared to release your grip if either casualty struggles further or you become exhausted

BUOYANT AID RESCUE

SEPARATING TWO CASUALTIES

WARNING! This method is very tiring and is not always physically possible. Only use it if you are very fit and strong. Keep to short distances.

DEFENSIVE STAND OFF POSITION

Defensive Methods

Defensive methods are used to enable you to keep away from a casualty or to prevent you being grasped suddenly by someone in difficulty. No defensive action is effective in every case. Variations of the methods described below may be necessary. The following methods have proved effective in a number of different situations:

- defensive stand-off position
- defensive reverse action
- defensive blocking actions (three methods)

Defensive Stand-Off Position

You should always use a defensive stand off position when approaching any conscious casualty; or when you need to assess or re-assess a situation from a swimming position in deep water.

- keep a safe distance, at least **three metres** away from the casualty
- take up an defensive position treading water
- push one leg forward, slightly bent
- scull with both hands to maintain your position in the water

Defensive Reverse Action

You should always use a defensive reverse action when a casualty attempts to grasp you.

- tuck the legs rapidly under the body and push them forward
- kick away vigorously, using your upper body, hands and arms to assist acceleration
- adopt the defensive stand-off position

DEFENSIVE REVERSE ACTION

Defensive Blocking Actions

You should always use one of the following defensive blocking actions when a casualty lunges forward suddenly before it is possible to reverse. Speed and vigour are essential.

- raise your rescue aid, arm or leg to block the casualty's movement
- push strongly and directly against the casualty's chest
- swim away or submerge
- adopt the defensive stand-off position

Defensive Rescue Aid Block

- block the casualty's forward movement with your rescue aid
- let go of the aid and reverse away
- adopt defensive stand-off position

Defensive Arm Block

- extend one or both arms and push against the casualty's upper chest
- reverse away vigorously
- adopt defensive stand-off position

Defensive Leg Block

- adopt a tuck position
- place your foot against the casualty's upper chest
- extend your leg and push the casualty away
- reverse away vigorously
- adopt defensive stand-off position

Practise all these methods on land and against a wall, before practising them in the water. Build speed and vigour slowly.

RESCUE AID BLOCK

ARM BLOCK

LEG BLOCK

ESCAPE FROM WRIST GRASP UNDERHOLD

Escape Methods

These methods require training and practice. They are useful in the following situations:

- when you have got yourself into difficulty by mistake
- when you are suddenly dragged into or underwater by another person

With proper training you should be able to avoid the first situation, while anticipation of the unexpected should give you a better chance of avoiding danger.

Escape Principles

- experiment with a variety of methods
- expect the unexpected
- apply direct force against a large target
- act quickly and vigorously
- always withdraw to a defensive stand-off position, after escaping

ESCAPE FROM WRIST GRASP UPPERHOLD

Escape from Wrist Grasp

You should use an escape from wrist grasp when one of your wrists is grasped by a casualty.

- clench the fist of the grasped arm
- take hold of it with your other hand
- pull the fist and arm upwards (if the casualty's hands are on the under side of your arm) or downwards (if the casualty's hands are on the upper side of your arm)
- reverse away vigorously out of reach
- adopt defensive stand-off position

6

ESCAPE FROM WRIST GRASP

Escape from Rear Grasp (1)

You should use this escape method if you are grasped from behind around the neck.

- as soon as you feel the grasp, take a deep breath
- tuck your chin into your chest to protect your throat
- grasp the casualty's elbow and wrist on the upper arm
- push up on the elbow and pull down on the wrist rapidly and vigorously
- push the casualty's arm up over your head
- as the grasp is broken, escape behind and away from the casualty
- adopt a defensive stand off position

ESCAPE FROM REAR GRASP 1

Escape from Rear Grasp (2)

You should use this escape method if you are grasped from behind around waist (your arms may be pinned in).

- take hold of a finger or thumb on each of the casualty's hands
- exert pressure against the joints to lever the hands apart
- push your elbows and hands outwards
- force the casualty's arms open wide
- release your grip, swim quickly out of reach
- adopt a defensive stand-off position

Escape from Front Grasp

You should use an escape from front grasp if you are grabbed from the front around the head, neck, chest, arms or body.

- start your escape immediately to prevent the casualty's legs wrapping round your body
- take a deep breath and tuck your chin into your chest
- extend your arms forcefully against the casualty's chest, armpits or waist
- duck away vigorously underwater and out of reach
- adopt defensive stand-off position

ESCAPE FROM REAR GRASP 2

ESCAPE FROM FRONT GRASP

Recovery Methods

Recovery of Submerged or Unconscious Casualty

If you have observed a casualty submerging prior to or during the approach, it may be possible to recover the body without too much delay, particularly if the casualty has submerged close to the side. However, poor and murky water conditions often make it impossible to recover a casualty quickly without specialist help. In these situations a systematic search will be necessary using diving equipment.

Sightings and Cross-Bearings

When a drowning casualty submerges in open water, you must make sure that you are wading or swimming in a straight line towards the casualty's last known position. Sighting and cross bearing are two methods for helping you to find the casualty.

To take a sighting, note where the casualty was last seen. Line up this position with a stationary object, such as a tree, a building or other environmental feature, on the far shore, before estimating the casualty's distance from the shore along that imaginary line.

When another rescuer is available, a cross bearing can be taken along the shore. Each rescuer takes a sighting on the position where the casualty was last seen. If other rescuers or bystanders are available, they can act as spotters from the shore. Wade or swim to the casualty, checking back with the spotters for directions.

Searching Shallow Water Areas

This is the only form of search that you can undertake without specialist assistance. While you could attempt to search a shallow water area on your own, it would be slow and painstaking work. To be most effective you require a number of volunteer rescuers.

To search shallow water areas with poor water clarity, organise a group of rescuers to link hands or hold hands and form a line in the water. The shortest rescuer should be in the shallowest water and the tallest rescuer in water that is no more than chest deep. The whole line should move across the area together. Start where the casualty was last seen.

As the search line moves forward, sweep your feet across the bottom with each step. Your search team must not go deeper than chest deep. Only trained lifeguards and other specialists should attempt to conduct a search in deeper areas.

Surface Diving

Where the casualty can be seen below the surface in deep water, you should perform a head first surface dive. Where the water is murky, it is safer to perform a feet first surface dive. Surface diving and swimming underwater are described in detail in Chapter 3.

WARNING!
Surface diving and underwater swimming are dangerous. Diving to a depth greater than 1.5 metres can damage your hearing. Taking repeated deep breaths may cause hyperventilation and loss of consciousness.

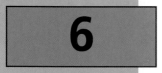

SHALLOW WATER SEARCH

Lifesaving

Reaching a Submerged Casualty

- surface dive to the casualty
- get into position close to the casualty's head
- grasp the casualty under both armpits
- push off the bottom to help your return to the surface (take care in mud and weeds)

Helping an Unconscious Casualty

An unconscious casualty is likely to be lying face down in the water. If the casualty has not stopped breathing immediately, respiration will cease within seconds. Speed, care and continuous observation are essential.

Turning an Unconscious Casualty

If you need to turn an unconscious casualty who is face down in the water:

- swim to the side of the casualty
- lift one shoulder and depress the other in order to rotate the casualty's body
- support the casualty's back and chin as you move the casualty into a towing position

Recovery and Care of a Spinal Injury Casualty

The recovery and care of a spinal injury casualty requires a number of trained and experienced rescuers or lifeguards. The management of an aquatic spinal injury demands considerable training and practice and the use of specialist skills. As a competent lifesaver, you should learn to recognise a spinal injury (see Chapter 5 under Casualty Recognition) and to take action appropriate to your training and expertise.

If you suspect a spinal injury, you should act as if a spinal injury is present. The exact care required will depend on the following factors:

- condition of the casualty (including whether breathing and a pulse are present)
- location of the casualty (deep or shallow water, above or below the surface)
- availability of assistance (trained rescuers, lifeguards, emergency services)
- environmental conditions (air and water temperature, waves and currents)

Unless you have completed specialist aquatic spinal injury management training (see other RLSS UK publications), take the following action:

- **telephone or send for specialist help**
- **talk to and reassure the casualty, if conscious, until help arrives**
- **avoid moving the casualty, as this may aggravate the injury further**

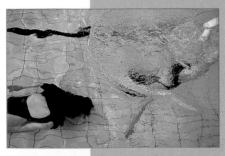

REACHING A SUBMERGED CASUALTY

WARNING!
Moving a casualty with a suspected spinal injury may cause extensive injury. Spinal injury management requires specialist training and assistance.

TURNING AN UNCONSCIOUS CASUALTY

Support Methods

Supporting an Unconscious or Conscious Casualty

Research has shown that during a rescue attempt, the casualty or rescuer may need support either through exhaustion or because expired air ventilation is needed or on reaching the side at the end of a swim. The following support methods are described below:

- **against firm support**
- **in deep water**
- **in shallow water**

Against Firm Support

You should use this method to support a casualty at the side or bank prior to landing; if you are exhausted and need time to recover; the casualty is unconscious and needs expired air ventilation.

- rest the casualty's head against your shoulder
- make contact with the point of support
- maintain contact with the casualty and point of support
- turn the casualty to face the support
- position the casualty close to and facing the support
- pass your arms, one at a time, under the casualty's armpits and take a firm grip of the support
- provide additional support by placing one knee between the casualty's thighs and resting your other leg against the side or bank
- support the casualty's head by resting it on one shoulder and maintaining a clear airway

AGAINST FIRM SUPPORT

Lifesaving

Support in Deep or Shallow Water

You can support a casualty in deep or shallow water if you are exhausted and need time to recover; a casualty is unconscious or injured; a support aid is available.

With a Buoyant Aid

- hold the buoyant aid in one hand
- rest the casualty's neck over your elbow joint
- support the casualty's chin with your free hand

Without a Buoyant Aid

- from the side of the casualty
- either support the neck and back of the head
- or support the jaw and the top of the head

Raising a conscious casualty's head clear of the water reduces fear and panic.

DEEP WATER SUPPORT WITH AID

DEEP WATER SUPPORT WITHOUT AID

6

Resuscitation in Water

During the course of a rescue, you may need to commence expired air ventilation (EAV) while still in the water. In some cases, this may be because the casualty has already stopped breathing when you arrive on the scene. Resuscitation in the water is not easy and requires regular practice. Calmness and urgency are needed.

Full cardiopulmonary resuscitation (CPR) involving chest compressions is virtually impossible in the water as it is hard to provide sufficient support for a casualty's back. Accounts of successful expired air ventilation in deep and shallow water, using the mouth-to-nose method, are well documented.

Key Principles

Before commencing resuscitation in the water:

- check the casualty's level of response, breathing and pulse
- check the casualty's mouth for obstructions
- decide whether resuscitation in the water is necessary
    - **YES** - casualty is unconscious and not breathing
    - **NO** - casualty is conscious or unconscious and breathing
- decide whether you would be better to tow the casualty to the side (you will be influenced by the time needed, the distance to be covered and the conditions affecting the rescue attempt)
- decide whether you have the strength, stamina and ability to perform expired air ventilation in the water

During resuscitation in the water, remember to:

- **support the casualty at all times**
- **keep the casualty's face clear of the water**
- **use the mouth-to-nose method of resuscitation**
- **maintain an effective seal and rhythm (about 10 inflations per minute)**

6

Resuscitation from Land or Boat

You should attempt to resuscitate a casualty from land or from a boat if you are unable to lift an unconscious, non-breathing casualty out of the water.

- lie flat on the bank or boat with your shoulders over the water
- support the casualty's shoulders with one hand
- support the casualty's chin with your other hand
- close the mouth, lift the jaw and extend the neck
- seal your mouth over the nose and start expired air ventilation

RESUSCITATION FROM THE LAND

Resuscitation when Standing in Shallow Water

You should only attempt resuscitation when standing in shallow water if a casualty is unconscious and not breathing and you can stand securely.

Unsupported (away from side, no aid available)

- stand to the side of casualty's head
- support the casualty's head and trunk with one hand under the far armpit
- close the mouth, lift the jaw and extend the neck with your other hand
- seal your mouth over the nose and start expired air ventilation

Supported (at side or using an aid)

- place the casualty sideways between you and the support
- **either** hold the support with one hand and support the casualty's head by placing it over the crook of one arm
- **or** rest the casualty's head on the same shoulder as your towing arm and slip your other arm under the casualty's neck and grasp the support
- close the mouth, lift the jaw and extend the neck with your other hand
- seal your mouth over the nose and start expired air ventilation

Resuscitation in Deep Water with Support

You should only attempt resuscitation in deep water if a casualty is unconscious and not-breathing and you are close to a support.

Supported (using land or a buoyant aid as support)

- place the casualty sideways between you and the support
- hold the support with one hand
- use one of the two methods for supporting the casualty described above
- close the mouth, lift the jaw and extend the neck with the other hand
- seal your mouth over the nose and start EAV
- tread water, preferably using an eggbeater kick (or push up on the side with your feet)
- kick hard out of the water to ensure you make an effective seal over the nose
- between inflations sink down into the water, relaxing and saving energy
- move the casualty, if necessary, by swimming smoothly and maintaining a regular inflation rhythm

Successful deep water resuscitation has been recorded only where the rescuer was using some type of support or buoyant aid. For further information on resuscitation methods, please refer to the RLSS UK publication 'Life Support'.

SUPPORTED RESUSCITATION

WARNING!
If the casualty is unconscious, not breathing and apparently has no pulse, it may be better to tow the casualty to the side as quickly as possible in order to carry out further checks and CPR on land. In cold water, it is very difficult to feel a casualty's pulse.

Casualty Landings

Landing a casualty is often the most difficult part of a rescue attempt. Help will almost certainly be needed to remove the casualty from the water to a position of safety, as you may be exhausted, the casualty heavy or unconscious and the land steep or slippery.

- keep your back straight when lifting
- use your thigh and leg muscles
- look after your body

Key Principles

- seek and use assistance, whenever possible
- look after your own safety (avoid lifting heavy loads)
- if exhausted or landing is impossible, support the casualty in the water until help arrives
- take care of the casualty's body and head throughout the landing
- keep the casualty horizontal and raise the legs above heart and head level, when rescuing from cold water
- move a conscious casualty away from the side and provide aftercare
- continue immediately with resuscitation on land for an unconscious, non-breathing casualty
- put an unconscious, breathing casualty in the recovery position and provide aftercare

Selecting the Best Method of Landing

A number of factors will affect your choice of landing. They include:

- your strength, height, fitness and experience
- condition, height and weight of the casualty
- range of environmental conditions (including weather, land conditions and help available)

In order to become competent at landing a casualty, you will need to practise all the techniques described below and be ready to select and adapt any landing method to suit your situation.

Gentle Slope Landings (shore, beach, shallow pool)
- assisted walk out
- pull ashore
- assisted carry

Steep Slope Landings (river, canal, dock, swimming pool)
- stirrup lift
- assisted lift
- horizontal lift

6

Gentle Slope Landings

Assisted Walk Out

You can use an assisted walk out when a casualty is exhausted but can walk with assistance.

- rest in shallow water
- slide your head under the casualty's armpit and one arm around the casualty's waist
- walk ashore supporting the casualty and then provide aftercare

ASSISTED WALK OUT

Pull Ashore

You can use a pull ashore landing when a casualty is unable to assist you and the shore is gently sloping.

- float the casualty to water of waist depth close to the shore
- call for assistance
- walk backwards supporting the casualty under the armpits, holding the wrists and making use of any available assistance
- place the casualty gently on the ground, in a safe position away from the water, and provide aftercare

PULL ASHORE

Assisted Carry

You can use an assisted carry when a casualty is unable to help but assistance is available.

- support the casualty under the armpits and take hold of the wrists
- call for assistance
- instruct your assistant to take hold of the legs and ankles of the casualty (if more than one helper is available, extra support can be given to the casualty's body)
- carry the casualty ashore
- place the casualty gently on the ground, in a safe position away from the water, and provide aftercare

ASSISTED CARRY

STIRRUP LANDING

Steep Slope Landings

Stirrup Lift

You can use a stirrup lift when a casualty is able to provide assistance.

- provide support against the bank until you and the casualty have recovered sufficiently to complete an effective landing
- move to the casualty's side or back
- reach down and cup one hand under the casualty's foot or knee, while maintaining a firm grip on the bank with your other hand (alternatively, you may be able to use your thigh as a step up)
- instruct the casualty clearly and simply how to climb out
- support the casualty during the landing
- move the casualty to a safe position away from the water and provide aftercare

Assisted Lift

You can use an assisted lift when a casualty is unable to assist and help from one or more bystanders is available.

- support the casualty against the side until you are ready for the landing
- call for assistance, take control of the situation and organise the landing
- keep the casualty facing the bank
- instruct your assistants to stay on the bank and take a firm hold of the casualty's wrists
- instruct at least one of your assistants to take care of the casualty's head throughout the lift
  - if any swimmers are in the water and available to help, instruct them to join you in lifting the casualty from the water by supporting the hips
  - on an agreed command, instruct everyone to lift the casualty at the same time
  - try to lift the casualty out of the water until the hips or thighs are level with the top of the bank
  - bend the casualty at the waist and lower the trunk to the ground, keeping both trunk and head well supported
  - lift the legs out of the water maintaining the support
  - instruct your assistants on land to move the casualty away from the water by turning the trunk and legs
  - move the casualty to safe position, place in the recovery position, if unconscious, and provide aftercare

ASSISTED LIFT

Horizontal Landing

You can use a horizontal landing when a casualty has been in cold water and is unable to assist with landing; a casualty is in shallow water or the water level is just below the top of the bank; help is available from one or more bystanders (and a board is available).

- support the casualty in the water until you are ready to start the landing
- call for assistance, take control of the situation and organise the landing
- instruct your assistants to enter the water (with a board if available) and join you in providing horizontal support for the casualty (see illustration) - it may be helpful to have a few assistants on land as well
- in shallow water, you will be able to lift the casualty (with or without a board) carefully and fairly easily on to the bank
- in deep water, this landing will only be possible if the top of the bank is level with, or at the very most a few centimetres, above the water level
- take firm control of the casualty (and the board) by instructing your assistants to place their arms under the casualty's body (assistance on land will probably be required)
- on an agreed command, lift or slide the casualty on to the top of the bank
- climb out, move the casualty carefully to a safe position away from the water
- place in the recovery position, if unconscious, and provide aftercare

HORIZONTAL LANDING

6

Training and Assessing Rescue Skills

Check your knowledge and understanding of rescue skills by answering the questions on the next page. You should join a recognised lifesaving or lifeguard club to practise and develop your ability as a competent rescuer.

Training

You should learn how and when to use these skills both in your local swimming pool and, under supervision, in open water environments. You should practise using the full range of rescue skills both individually and with others. You should focus on improving your fitness, knowledge and judgement as you become more familiar with each specific technique. Your ability to become a competent lifesaver will improve with practice, experience and time.

Assessing

You should test your ability to use these rescue skills on a regular basis by taking one of the many RLSS UK trainer assessed rescue awards or by attempting to gain one of the major lifesaving awards which includes a number of challenging rescue elements.

LAND BASED RESCUE

6

Checking your Understanding of Rescue Skills

The following questions are designed to test your knowledge and understanding of rescue principles and skills, as described in this chapter; alongside each question is the relevant page reference.

6

OPEN WATER RESCUE

RESCUE SEQUENCE

shout

↓

signal

↓

reach

↓

throw

↓

wade

↓

row

↓

swim with an aid

↓

swim and tow

6

Summary

Rescue skills are simple and effective; they are easily adapted to suit different conditions and casualties. They require regular practice but once mastered can make the difference between life and death. Wherever you go and whatever situation you find yourself in, always remember to look after your own safety before following the simple rules of the rescue sequence.

SUPPORTED RESCUE

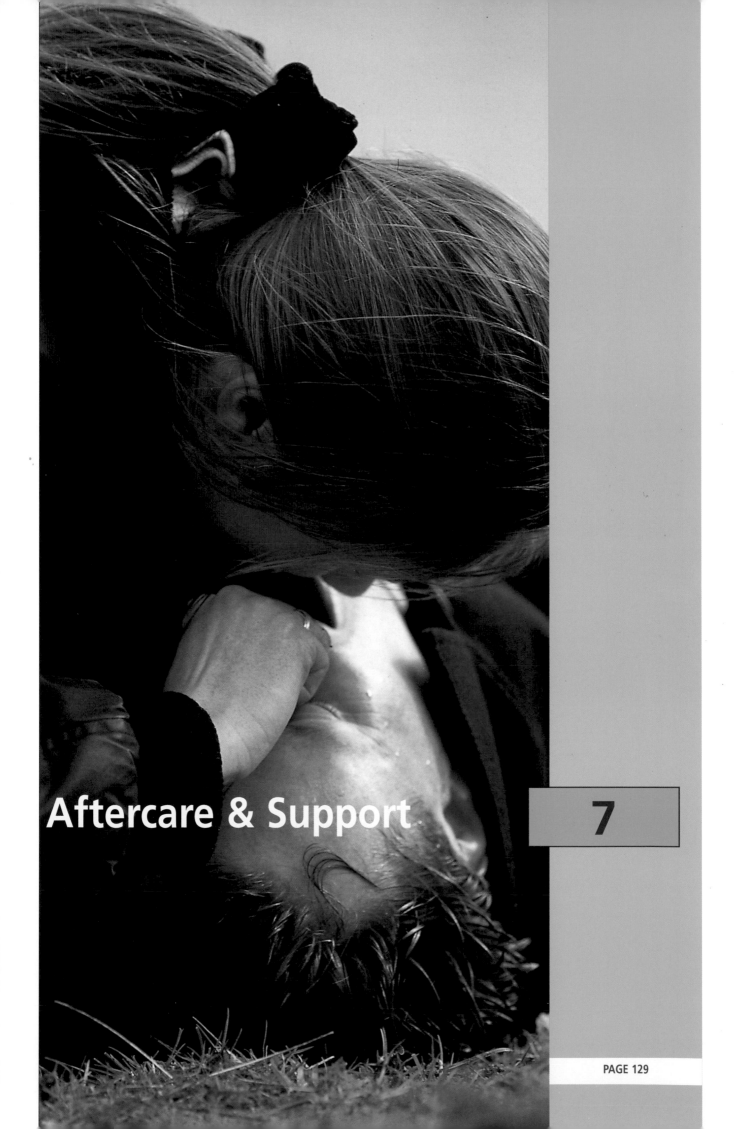

Aftercare & Support

Introduction to Aftercare & Support

This chapter provides guidance on the different types of aftercare and support rescuers, casualties and bystanders are likely to need during and after an emergency situation. You will find brief explanations of the following:

- emergency aftercare
- life support
- aquatic first aid
- post traumatic stress awareness
- outcomes of rescues
- learning from your experiences
- counselling and support
- aftercare training
- assessing aftercare skills

For further information and guidance, please refer to the RLSS UK publication, 'Life Support', which contains specialist text and illustrations on the key aspects of emergency aftercare, basic life support and first aid.

EMERGENCY AFTERCARE

Emergency Aftercare & Support

Immediately following a rescue, you must act quickly, calmly and correctly in order to save life and prevent the casualty's condition deteriorating. In many cases, it is this action which will guarantee a casualty's survival.

Recent tragedies and disasters have proved that it is not just those involved directly in an emergency situation who may need aftercare and support, but often witnesses to the scene may need counselling and guidance.

The priorities of emergency aftercare are as follows:

- **expired air ventilation**
- **cardiopulmonary resuscitation (CPR)**
- **management of choking**
- **control of bleeding**
- **care of an unconscious, breathing casualty**
- **treatment for shock**

After landing a casualty, you should check the condition of the casualty and confirm that the casualty is breathing before treating injuries.

7

Life Support Sequence

For detailed descriptions and illustrations of the life support sequence for adults, children and babies, please refer to the RLSS UK publication 'Life Support' (3rd Edition). The chart below shows the general life support sequence to follow in an emergency.

initial action
- ensure the safety of yourself and the casualty
- check whether the casualty is responsive

if responsive
- check for injuries
- reassess at intervals
- obtain help if needed

if unresponsive
- shout for help
- open airway
- check whether casualty is breathing

if unresponsive but breathing
- turn into the recovery position
- telephone for help

if not breathing
- send or go for help
- give 2 breaths of rescue breathing
- check casualty's pulse

if unresponsive and not breathing, but pulse present
- continue rescue breathing
- check pulse every minute

if unresponsive and no pulse (drowning or injured casualty, child or baby)
- perform cardiopulmonary resuscitation for 1 minute, then go for help
(for other adult casualties)
- go for help immediately
- perform continuous cardiopulmonary resuscitation

LIFE SUPPORT ON LAND

Aquatic First Aid

The aims of first aid are:

- **to preserve life**
- **to minimise the effects of injury**
- **to promote recovery**
- **to obtain further qualified assistance without delay**

After landing a casualty and carrying out the checks described on the previous page, consider whether you need to:

- place the casualty in the recovery position
- apply direct pressure to a bleeding injury
- care for broken limbs
- treat for hypothermia
- treat for shock

Detailed descriptions of how to place a casualty in the recovery position and provide first aid treatment can be found in the RLSS UK publication 'Life Support' and the 'First Aid Manual' of St John Ambulance, St Andrew's Ambulance Association and The British Red Cross Society.

CARING FOR AN UNCONSCIOUS CASUALTY

Around the waters of the United Kingdom and Ireland, the two most common treatments, after immersion in cold water, will be for shock and hypothermia.

Treatment for Shock

- lay the casualty with legs raised in a supine position if conscious or in the recovery position if unconscious
- keep the casualty warm enough to prevent heat loss
- avoid giving food and drink in case the casualty needs hospital treatment
- send for help without delay

Treatment for Hypothermia

Someone who is suffering from the effects of cold or hypothermia should be handled very gently and re-warmed slowly.

Take the following actions for a **conscious casualty**:

- remove the casualty from the water
- shelter the casualty from wind and rain immediately
- send for help
- create a warm, dry, sheltered place
- remove wet clothing and wrap in blankets, space blankets or a sleeping bag
- huddle together for warmth so the body temperature can rise gradually
- give warm, sweet drinks
- seek medical assistance as soon as possible

Take the following actions for an **unconscious casualty**:

- remove the casualty from the water
- shelter the casualty from wind and rain immediately
- send for help
- give expired air ventilation if the casualty is not breathing but has a pulse
- give cardiopulmonary resuscitation if the casualty is not breathing and has no pulse
- if the casualty starts breathing, place in the recovery position and provide aftercare
- create a warm, dry, sheltered place
- remove wet clothing and wrap in blankets or a sleeping bag
- seek medical assistance as soon as possible

Avoid excessive external heat (for example fire, electric blanket, radiators); **avoid** massaging arms and legs; **avoid** giving alcohol or drugs; **avoid** moving the casualty without medical assistance.

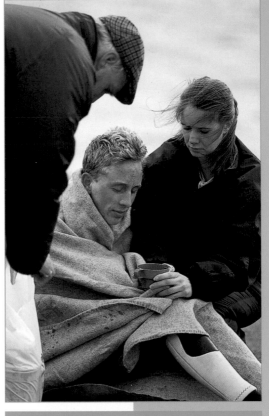

CARING FOR A COLD CASUALTY

7

Post Traumatic Stress Awareness

Many people suffer a delayed reaction to events that they have witnessed or experienced. Often they may appear outwardly calm during an emergency situation, yet later can experience a range of emotions varying from complete euphoria to depression, nightmares or shock.

In general, as each person is physically different, so individuals will react differently to the same experience. You need to be aware that how someone seems to be reacting to events is not necessarily how they are feeling inside.

Outcomes of Rescues

Many rescues are successful, many casualties recover, many lives are saved; yet there are times when, through no fault of the rescuer, the attempted rescue is unsuccessful.

As you learn from the practice and experience of different rescue scenarios, so you should discuss and reflect on what happens with your training partners. In training yourself to cope with the past and the present you are preparing yourself to cope with the future.

You should be prepared emotionally as well as physically for success and failure. You should learn to deal positively with what happens to you and develop an inner strength in recognising and confronting the feelings of elation and depression which are the natural outcomes of intense physical and emotional experiences.

Learning from your Experiences

The following agenda may be helpful to you when discussing and reflecting on your rescue experiences:

- describe what you saw
- describe what you did
- describe the reasons for your actions
- describe how you felt
- describe how you feel now
- consider your feelings of:
  - frustration
  - sadness
  - anger
  - guilt
  - lack of control
  - elation
  - "what if..."
  - "if only..."
- discuss your reactions to the emergency situation
- discuss the possible and actual outcomes
- develop plans and strategies for coping with, using and developing the experiences that you have encountered

7

Counselling and Support

Many organisations, local authorities and emergency services now provide specialist counselling services and advice for victims of human tragedies and disasters. A list of addresses is supplied at the back of this handbook.

Coping with Stress

In the first twenty four hours after the incident:

- alternate physical exercise with relaxation
- keep busy, do things you enjoy while allowing time to relax and unwind
- keep communicating and spending time with others
- remember people care
- if you feel unhappy, share your feelings and emotions, talk to someone
- remind yourself that your reaction is normal
- watch your diet, cut down on sugars, fats and caffeine
- avoid alcohol and drugs
- keep to your normal routine as much as possible

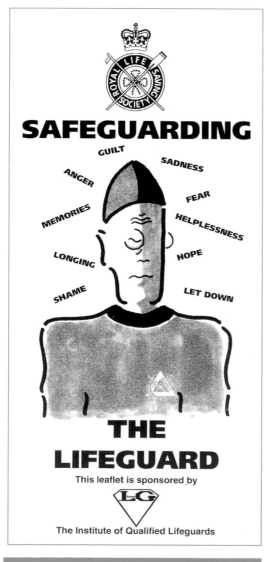

RLSS UK POST TRAUMATIC STRESS LEAFLET

7

Training and Assessing Aftercare and Support Skills

Check your knowledge and understanding of aftercare by answering the questions below. Join a recognised lifesaving or lifeguard club to practise and develop your skills.

Training

You should participate in a varied aftercare education programme which gives you opportunity to learn and practise your life support, basic first aid and initiative skills. You will need to learn how to identify different types of casualty and how to react to changes in a casualty's condition.

Assessing

You should test your knowledge, understanding and ability to provide aftercare and support by taking one of the many RLSS UK life support or aquatic first aid awards.

Checking your Understanding of Aftercare & Support

The following questions are designed to check your knowledge and understanding of aftercare & support, as described in this chapter; alongside each question is the relevant page reference.

page 130	What are the priorities of emergency aftercare?
page 131	What should you do if a casualty is responsive?
page 131	What should you do if a casualty is unresponsive?
page 131	What should you do if a casualty has a pulse but is not breathing?
page 131	What should you do if a casualty has no pulse?
page 132	What are the aims of first aid?
page 133	How would you treat a casualty suffering from hypothermia?
page 134	What is post traumatic stress?
page 135	What should you do to cope with stress?

Summary

Aftercare and support skills are as important as the skills needed in a rescue attempt. Often the aftercare provision of life support and basic first aid, of medical assistance and counselling, will make the difference between full recovery and death for a casualty. Continue practising your skills and keep up-to-date with developments in aftercare.

CALLING FOR HELP

Lifesaving Reference

8

RLSS UK Awards Programme

The Royal Life Saving Society United Kingdom has a comprehensive awards and training programme offering challenges and qualifications in all aspects of lifesaving, lifeguarding and life support to people of all ages and abilities. The current programme is aimed at:

- Schools and Colleges
- Community Groups and Organisations
- Individual Members of the Society
- Lifesaving and Lifeguard Clubs
- Lifeguards at Coastal & Inland Open Water Locations
- Lifeguards in Public and Private Swimming Pools
- Leisure and Sports Centres
- Outdoor Activity Centres
- Swimming Teachers
- Police and Emergency Services
- Teachers, Trainers and Assessors
- Members of the General Public

The awards are designed to provide a framework for challenging each participant in the programme and for developing knowledge, understanding and ability in the principles and skills of lifesaving, lifeguarding and life support.

Many of the Society's awards are recognised as the standard qualifications for professional and voluntary employment in the areas of pool and beach lifeguarding as well as in supervisory and teaching activities. At present, the Society offers awards in:

- Water Safety
- Survival & Self Rescue
- Swimming
- Rescue
- Lifesaving
- Pool Lifeguarding
- Beach Lifeguarding
- Life Support
- Emergency Response
- Training
- Assessing
- Competition

For further details regarding the current RLSS UK awards programme, its award conditions and assessment procedures, please contact Mountbatten House .

8

8

Bibliography

The following publications are recommended for further reading and reference:

RLSS UK Publications

Beach Lifeguarding *(RLSS UK 1994)*
Life Support *(Mosby Lifeline 1997)*
National Curriculum Swimming & Water Safety Pack & Video *(RLSS UK 1993)*
Pool Lifeguard *(Mosby Lifeline 1997)*
Rescues in the British Isles *(RLSS UK 1988)*
Swim, Survive, Save *(Mosby Lifeline 1996)*
Rookie Trainer's Guide *(Mosby Lifeline 1997)*
Safety on British Beaches *(RLSS UK & RoSPA 1993)*
Specially Safe *(RLSS UK 1995)*

Other Publications

American Red Cross **Basic Water Safety** *(American Red Cross 1988)*
American Red Cross **Lifeguarding Today** *(American Red Cross 1992)*
American Red Cross **Swimming and Diving** *(American Red Cross 1992)*
ASA **National Curriculum Resource Pack for Swimming and Water Safety** *(ASA 1993)*
Austin G. **Swimming for Fitness** *(A&C Black 1990)*
British Heart Foundation **Heartstart UK- Emergency Life Support Training Pack** *(BHF 1993)*
British Red Cross et al **First Aid Manual** *(Dorling Kindersley 1993)*
Counsilman J. **Competitive Swimming Manual for Coaches and Swimmers** *(Pelham 1978)*
Counsilman J. **The Science of Swimming** *(Pelham 1969)*
Cross R. (Ed) **ASA Guide to Better Swimming** *(PAN Books 1987)*
Cross R. (Ed) **Swimming Teaching and Coaching: Level One** *(ASA 1991)*
Cross R. (Ed) **Swimming Teaching and Coaching: Level Two** *(ASA 1993)*
Davies S. **Learn to Swim in a Weekend** *(Dorling Kindersley 1993)*
Donlan A. **Survival in Cold Water** *(ASA 1989)*
Garratt P. **Flexibility for Swimming** *(Kaye & Ward 1980)*
Health & Safety Executive **Safety in Swimming Pools** *(Sports Council 1988)*
ISRM **Diving in Swimming Pools** *(ISRM 1990)*
Juba K & Wilkie D. **The Handbook of Swimming** *(Pelham 1986)*
Maglischo E. **Swimming Faster** *(Mayfield Publishing Company 1982)*
Meaney P. (Ed) **Teaching Swimming and Water Safety** *(AUSTSWIM 1993)*
Norman S. & Pollard A. **What's in a Game?** *(SPLASH 1988)*
Orme N. **Early British Swimming 55 BC-AD 1719** *(University of Exeter 1983)*

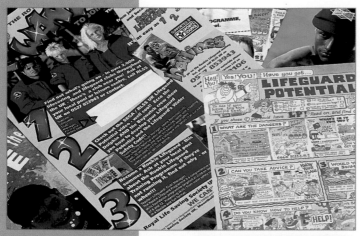

RLSS UK PUBLICITY MATERIALS

Lifesaving

Useful Addresses

RLSS UK
Mountbatten House
Studley
Warwickshire
B80 7NN
Tel (01527) 853943
Fax (01527) 854453

Amateur Swimming Association
Harold Fern House
Derby Square
Loughborough
Leicestershire
LE11 0AL
Tel (01509) 230431
Fax (01509) 610720

British Canoe Union
Adbolton Lane
West Bridgford
Nottingham
NG2 5AS
Tel (01602) 821100
Fax (01602) 821797

British Heart Foundation
14 Fitzhardinge Street
London
W1H 4DH
Tel (0171) 935.0185
Fax (0171) 486 1273

British Red Cross
National Headquarters
9 Grosvenor Crescent
London
SW1X 7EF
Tel (0171) 235 5454
Fax (0171) 245 6315

British Sub-Aqua Club
Telford's Quay
Ellesmere Port
South Wirral
L65 4FY
Tel (0151) 357 1951
Fax (0151) 357 1250

British Water-Ski Federation
390 City Road
London
EC1V 2QA
Tel (0171) 833 2855
Fax (0171) 837 5879

HM Coastguard
Spring Place
105 Commercial Road
Southampton
SO15 IEG
Tel (01703) 329100
Fax (01703) 329488

Institute of Leisure and Amenity Management (ILAM)
Ilam House
Lower Basildon
Reading
Berkshire
RG8 9NE
Tel (01491) 874222
Fax (01491) 874059

International Lifesaving Federation
Hogeschuol Plein 2.
3000 Leuven
Belgium
Tel 00 32 16239494
Fax 00 32 16295194

Useful Addresses

Institute of Qualified Lifeguards
RLSS UK
Mountbatten House
Studley
Warwickshire
B80 7NN
Tel (01527) 853943
Fax (01527) 854453

Institute of Sport and Recreation
Management (ISRM)
Giffard House
36/38 Sherrard Street
Melton Mowbray
Leicestershire
LE13 1XJ
Tel (01664) 65531
Fax (01664) 501155

Institute of Swimming Teachers
and Coaches
Dawson House
63 Forest Road
Loughborough
Leicestershire
LE11 3NW
Tel (01509) 264357
Fax (01509) 219349

South Africa Lifesaving
Association
Surf House
35 Livingstone Road
Durban 4001
South Africa
Tel 0027 31 239251
Fax 0027 31 235612

St. Andrew's Ambulance
Association
St Andrew's House
Milton Street
Glasgow
64 OHR
Tel 0141 332 4031
Fax 0141 332 6582

St. John Ambulance
1 Grosvenor Crescent
London
SW1X 7EJ
Tel (0171) 235 5231
Fax (0171) 235 0796

Swimming Teachers' Association
Anchor House
Birch Street
Walsall
WS2 8HZ
Tel (01922) 645097
Fax (01922) 720628

Royal Humane Society
Brettenham House
Lancaster Place
London
WC2E 7EP
Tel (0171) 836 8155

RLSS Australia
PO Box 1567
North Sydney
New South Wales 2059
Australia
Tel 00612 957 4799
Fax 00612 929 5726

8

RLSS Canada
287 McArthur Avenue
Ottawa
Ontario
Canada K1L 6P3
Tel 001 613 746 5694
Fax 001 613 746 9929

RLSS Commonwealth
Headquarters
4 Windsor Court
Greenhill Street
Stratford-Upon-Avon
CV37 6GG
Tel (01789) 295222
Fax (01789) 295223

RLSS New Zealand
PO Box 13-489
Christchurch
New Zealand
Tel and Fax 00643 366 7644

THE LIFESAVER'S BEST FRIEND ?

Royal National Lifeboat Institution (RNLI)
Headquarters
West Quay Road
Poole
Dorset
BH15 1HZ
Tel (01202) 671133
Fax (01202) 670128

Royal Society for the Prevention of Accidents (RoSPA)
Cannon House
The Priory Queensway
Birmingham
B4 6BS
Tel (0121) 200 2461
Fax (0121) 200 1254

Royal Yachting Association
RYA House
Romsey Road
Eastleigh
Hampshire
SO50 9YA
Tel (01703) 627400
Fax (01703) 629924

Surf Life Saving Association of Great Britain (SLSA)
15 Sidwell Street
Exeter
Devon
EX14 6RY
Tel (01392) 54364
Fax (01392) 496563

Glossary of Terms

Aftercare   Assistance for a casualty provided by a rescuer, bystander or qualified medic following an emergency

Asphyxia   Insufficient oxygen reaching the tissues of the body

Bystander   A person present at an emergency situation who is not directly involved in the rescue, but who may be able to provide assistance when requested to do so

Buoyancy Jacket   Jacket with minimum buoyancy of 6kgs used for inland and supervised aquatic activities

CPR   Cardiopulmonary Resuscitation

Casualty   A person in difficulty at an emergency situation who needs assistance

Contact Rescue   A method of recovering a casualty from the water in situations where rescue aids are unavailable or unsuitable for use

Cross Bearings   Technique for determining where a casualty was last seen, performed by two rescuers some distance apart, pointing to a position where the lines of their pointing cross

Drowning   Death caused by asphyxia due to immersion in water

EAP   Emergency Action Plan

EAV   Expired Air Ventilation

First Aid   Initial or emergency help given to a casualty before qualified medical assistance is available

H.E.L.P.   Heat Escape Lessening Posture

Huddle   A survival position for groups of two or more persons wearing lifejackets, personal flotation devices or holding buoyancy aids for support

Hyperventilation   Deliberate or involuntary breathing when taking a series of deep breaths in rapid succession. This decreases the level of carbon dioxide, reduces the blood flow to brain and causes dizziness, unconsciousness and, occasionally, seizures.

Hyperthermia   Increase in the body's inner core temperature above its normal temperature. This causes weakness and dizziness including confusion and unconsciousness.

Hypothermia   Reduction in the body is inner core temperature to 35°C or below. This causes shivering, disorientation and possibly unconsciousness.

Lifesaving

Land Based Rescue Method of recovering a casualty without the rescuer entering the water

Lifeguard Qualified professional or volunteer employed to supervise and provide safety cover in swimming pools or open water locations

Lifejacket Jacket, with inherent buoyancy (min 6kg inflating to 16kg), designed to save life by keeping wearer face upwards and providing support in this position, suitable for use in the sea and other open water environments

Lifesaver A person who is prepared to assist anyone in difficulty or has ensured the safety and survival of a casualty

Life Support Resuscitation of an unconscious, non-breathing casualty

Non-Contact Rescue Method of recovering a casualty using a rescue aid without making direct physical contact

NOP Normal Operating Procedure

PFD Personal flotation device (lifejacket or buoyancy jacket)

Post Traumatic Stress Physical and emotional disorder caused by excessive amounts of stress during and after an emergency situation

Recovery Position Position in which an unconscious casualty is placed to allow observation and prevent obstruction of the airway

Resuscitation Act of reviving a nearly dead or apparently dead casualty

Rescue Method of recovering a casualty in difficulty

RNLI Royal National Lifeboat Institution

RoSPA Royal Society for the Prevention of Accidents

Shock Failure of the circulation which results in an inadequate supply of blood to the vital organs

Sighting Technique for noting where a casualty was last seen, performed by imagining a line to the opposite shore and estimating the casualty's position along that line

Water Based Rescue Method of recovering a casualty where it is necessary for the rescuer to enter the water or launch a craft on the water

Water Safety Sensible advice for ensuring the well being and protection of persons on, in or around water

8

Index

Index

8

Index

8